BROADSWORD

Monthly

Version 1.1 PDF July 2020
Version 1.0 Print July 2020

BROADSWORD

ADVENTURES FOR FIFTH EDITION

JULY 2020 ISSUE 7 Monthly

COVER: The shepherd monk Dai Zheng takes a moment to reflect near a waterfall in Aegreya's Jīn Forest. Art by Vagelio Kaliva.

July was insane.

In addition to releasing this book, we fulfilled a few thousand shipments, ran a successful Kickstarter, increased our Patreon to our highest numbers yet, built some amazing relationships with other major players in the space, and started creating new and more awesome products.

And it wasn't easy. Of course, COVID-19 is still the hot topic in the news. And the United States, where most of the staff lives, has had an interesting period of self-reflection hit it. Plus, we've had growing pains, too.

Regardless, we've made it through in one piece. And you made it with us. Thank you for being a patron, backer, subscriber, and customer. There will always be a light so long as you are at the end.

-Dave Hamrick

With the publication of this issue I am become Executive Editor of BroadSword, in addition to my previous duties as Art Director et al. What this means for you is that Dave has more time to write more outstanding adventure content for 5E. As Dave mentions above, these past few months have been a busy time for us, and we've been working out the kinks of a young, expanding organization. Rest assured we will continue to provide the excellent content you have come to expect from BroadSword Monthly!

-Scott Craig

VOL. I, NO. 7

EXEC EDITOR Scott Craig
EDITOR Benjamin Gilyot
HEAD WRITER Dave Hamrick
PROOFREADING Benjamin Gilyot & select DMDave patrons
TYPESETTING Scott Craig
LAYOUT Scott Craig
ART DIRECTOR Scott Craig
MARKETING Wayfinder
LOGISTICS Jennifer Craig
DMDAVE OPS Theresa Malan

CARTOGRAPHY Cze&Peku, Maps by Owen, Dyson Logos, Dave Hamrick, Watabou.itch.io, Darryl T. Jones, Jog Brogzin, Tom Cartos **ART** Matias Lazaro, Rick Hershey, Miguel Santos, Griffons Saddlebag, Jason Glover, David Johnson, William McAusland, Luigi Castellani, Joyce Maureira, Paper Forge, Maciej Zigorski, Titan Forge, Dean Spencer, Vagelio Kaliva.

BroadSword Monthly is Copyright 2019 Hamrick Brands, LLC
BroadSword Template Design by Scott Craig www.vaultofwonders.games

We are born to be, if we please, rational creatures, but it is use and exercise only that makes us so, and we are indeed so no farther than industry and application has carried us.

- John Locke

BEHIND THE SCREEN

HOW TO WRITE 5E ADVENTURES PART 3 - CREATING AN ENTICING CALL TO ACTION

BY DAVE HAMRICK
ART BY WILLIAM MCAUSLAND

This is the third part of my "How to Write 5e Adventures" series which debuted in *BroadSword Monthly #5*. In issue *#6* I discussed the outline of an adventure. This time I want to take a closer look at Calls to Action.

A Call to Action is the part of the story that introduces the adventure hook. It's the part of the story that ignites the desire in both the players and characters to solve the problem at hand.

Introduce The Problem

Above all, the Call to Action introduces a problem to the adventurers. Classic examples include:

- An NPC has been captured.
- The villain stole an important item.
- A specific item is rumored to be in the area.
- Someone important has gone missing in the area.
- A specific monster poses a threat to the character's objectives.
- Recently, a strange phenomenon has occurred in the area.
- The characters cannot continue their adventures until they receive help/information from someone important.

Of course, there are multiple variations on these tropes, but overall, most adventure hooks conform to these models.

Introduce the Stakes

Problems aren't always enough to get the characters interested in a problem. The characters and their players must both have a vested interest in the problem's negative outcome. For example, there could be an important noble who has gone missing. However, the noble was thought to be a bit of a crude bureaucrat who's made the lives of those who live in his city hell. The characters might not be interested in helping such a scad. But if the noble also had important information the characters need to continue their quest, now they have to put their feelings aside and rescue the noble.

If you aren't sure what motivates the characters, take a look at their character sheets. Backgrounds, ideals, and bonds are key in the development of problems and stakes. That assumes that the player focuses on these narrative features, of course. Even then, if you have a player who overlooks the background details of their character, you can always appeal to the players' desires. If the player is interested in loot and XP for their character, you might suggest that the deadly dragon that lives in the hills has an impressive treasure hoard. Or if a player enjoys exploration, they might be intrigued by the hook if it means they get to traipse through ancient dungeon ruins.

Set the Scene

Once you know what the problem is and what it will take to get the characters involved, introduce the hook through a scene. Since this is a roleplaying game, it's okay to use the direct approach. A town crier could announce the news of the missing noble or a mysterious cloaked figure can offer a large sum of gold to handle the dragon in the hills. You can also introduce the adventure hook through a scene that shows more than tells. For example, the characters go to meet the noble who has important information for them, dreading it as they walk to his estate. When they arrive, they discover a crime scene—and the noble is missing! Tracks lead away from the estate into the sewers. Or while they're wandering down a forest road, a gang of kobolds attacks the characters. They kobolds wear the markings of Red Scale the Dragon. It won't take long for the characters to track the kobolds back to Red Scale's lair.

Optional: Introduce Additional Stakes

As the scene plays out, make sure that the players are invested in what's happening. The best way to tell if they care is if they seem genuinely concerned—as players, not characters! Even negative emotions and cursing—"damn it, I can't believe we have to save this asshole to learn the location of the Crystal Goblet"—lets you know that you're headed the right way (within reason, of course). If they don't seem to care, toss in additional rewards. Maybe the local constable offers the characters 500 gp to find the noble? Or perhaps one of the characters' romantic interests promises his hand in marriage if they can thwart Red Scale?

Next: How to Create Story Objectives

USING THIS BOOK
GETTING THE MOST FROM BROADSWORD MONTHLY

BY DAVE HAMRICK
ART BY DYSON LOGOS AND WILLIAM MCAUSLAND

Must-have Tomes

To run this adventure, you will need access to the Fifth Edition rules and associated rulebooks.

Understanding the Format

> Text that appears in a box like this is meant to be read aloud or paraphrased for the players when their characters first arrive at a location or under a specific circumstance, as described in the text.

In addition to the monsters included in the core rulebooks, you will also need to use the content found in the Appendices of this book.

When a creature's name appears in **bold** type, that's a visual cue pointing you to its stat block in the core rulebooks. If a stat block appears as part of this book, the adventure's text tells you so.

Spells and equipment mentioned in the adventure are described in the core rulebooks. *Magic items* are also described in the core rulebooks unless the adventure's text directs you to an exclusive item that comes with this book.

Abbreviations

The following abbreviations are used throughout this adventure:

hp = hit points
AC = Armor Class
DC = Difficult Class
XP = experience points
pp = platinum piece(s)
gp = gold piece(s)
ep = electrum piece(s)
sp = silver piece(s)
cp = copper piece(s)
NPC = nonplayer character
PC = player character

LG = Lawful Good
NG = Neutral Good
CG = Chaotic Good
LN = Lawful Neutral
N = Neutral

CN = Chaotic Neutral
LE = Lawful Neutral
NE = Neutral evil
CE = Chaotic evil Ω

DELVING INTO DEEP DUNGEONS WITH DYSON

 Natural Wall
 Worked Wall
 Archway
 Doorway
 Secret Door
 Stairs
 Natural or Rough Stairs
 False Door
 Passage Underneath
 Trapdoor in Floor

 Secret Trap Door
 Double Door
 Elevated Ledge
 Ledge with Ramp Down
 Ruined Wall
 Lake or Pool
 Battlements
 Ladder
 Statue
 Pillars or Columns

 Bars or Portcullis
 Pit Trap
 Curtains or Tapestry
 Trap or Trap Trigger
 Boxes and Barrels
 Bed or Cot
 Table and Chairs
 Throne and Dais
 Altar

 Stone Bridge
 Rope & Wood Bridge
 Sloped Elevation
 Crypts
 Sarcophagus
 Small Ledges
 Crevasse
 Cave Under Ledge
 Debris, Rocks or Scree

See all of these icons interacting with each other at
http://rpgcharacters.wordpress.com/maps

OMERIA GAZETTEER
A CATALOGUE OF INTERESTING LOCALES

BY DAVE HAMRICK
ART BY WILLIAM MCAUSLAND
CARTOGRAPHY BY MAPS BY OWEN

The Continent of Omeria and Environs

Omeria is a land of mystery and high adventure. Herein you may find an overview of some of the most interesting locations.

Aegreya

A large island off the coast of The Summer Land, Aegreya is home to the Great Chromatics and their draconic descendants.

Aspaeth

The first major colony settled by the Pressonians, Aspaeth fell into ruin following the Transmuter Wars of the early 7th century.

Black Swamps of Barkor

These vile, lifeless mires surround Shred, the home of the danaavrakt. Contested Lands

Once part of the fallen nation of Karnione, the Contested Lands are locked in a four-way civil dispute between the nation of Dorithell and the city-states of Ingum, Nadorith, and Naqqad.

Dar

Also known as the Isle of Winds, Dar is a trading nexus for all of eastern Omeria.

Desolation of Ditimaya

This colossal desert that reaches coast to coast in Central Omeria was once a fertile savannah. The Tadju Confederacy rules the northern end of the desert.

Dorithell

The Exile Nation of Dorithell is ruled by the Dinzer lich Fazel Rastkar.

Elsath

Often classified as a "large island", the continent of Elsath is a land of untamed beauty and danger.

Fairknot Region

The Kingdoms of Man—Desneorus, Knotside, and Murktown—call this region surrounding the Fairknot River home.

Hag Peninsula

A haven for pirates, bandits, and assassins, the Hag Peninsula's greatest defense is its position relative to the Obsidian Plain and the Wither.

Karnione

Believed to be the oldest human nation in Omeria, possibly predating Presson's Enclave and The Summer Land, Karnione's once-great cities have been absorbed by The Wither.

Majiambayo Hayamalizi

Also known as The Sea of Man, these waters are heavily patrolled by Dinzer warships both on and over the water.

Majiambayo Hulumtu

Meaning "The Sea of Arms" in the Dinzer tongue, this great ocean hugs Odonburg's eastern and southern coasts.

Obsidian Plain

Dividing The Wither and Desolation of Ditimaya, the Obsidian Plain is recognizable by its jagged mountains, angry volcanoes, and merciless inhabitants.

Ocean of Warna

The largest ocean to the east of Omeria is home to the Marid-ruled nation of Qhek.

continued on page 8...

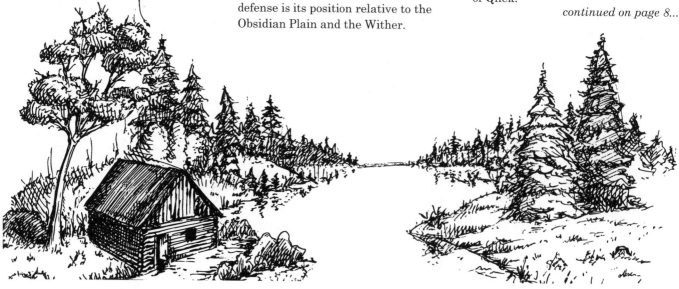

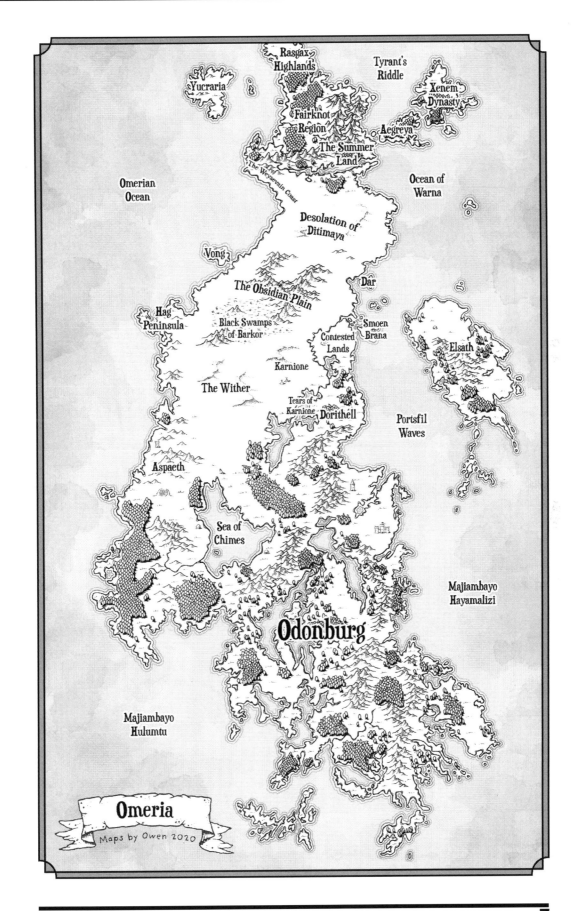

Omeria

Maps by Owen 2020

Odonburg

The most magically advanced nation in all of Omeria, Odonburg takes up roughly one-third of Omeria.

Omerian Ocean

The cruel, impassable ocean to Omeria's west bears the continent's name.

Portsfil Waves

The large body of water sandwiched between the Ocean of Warna and Majiambayo Hulumtu has long been a battleground between the Marids of Qhek and the elves of Ebirai.

Rasgax Highlands

Dangerous to most humans, the unsettled lands north of the Fairknot Region are home to the Rasgax tribes.

Sea of Chimes

The Dinzer tribes built their first villages along this great sea.

Smoen Brana

Once Karniothian slaves, the dogfolk canids call this rocky island nation home.

Summer Land

Along with the tribes of Odonburg, The Summer Land is the only early human nation that remains. It is ruled by the Pressonians of Presson's Enclave.

The Wither

Those who've never traveled to The Wither often mistake it as part of the Desolation of Ditimaya. Of course, The Wither is far more dangerous than Ditimaya or even the Obsidian Plain.

Tears of Karnione

The body of water which the ruined Nation of Karnione once filled with its sailing vessels is now the site of regular naval battles between the Contested Land's challengers.

Tyrant's Riddle

Tyrant's Riddle is the large body of water north of Aegreya and Xenem Dynasty.

Vong

Vong, the Black Claw, was once a powerful Pressonian colony a few miles off the Scorched Coast. Many of the horrors borne from the Transmuter Wars now hide in the blackened ruins of its fallen cities.

Weysevain Coast

Second only to Odonburg in population, the Weysevain Coast is home to the city-states of Arruquetta, Cabal, and Castlegrasp. Along with Tadju, these three realms are seen as the Four Great Powers of Central Omeria.

Xenem Dynasty

Xenem is a vampire-controlled island known for its extensive slave trade.

Yucraria

Sometimes referred to as "The Fierce Lands", Yucraria is the home of the wanderer halflings. Ω

TITAN'S
HEIR

CHAPTER 3: GRIHOO

BY DAVE HAMRICK

3rd-Level Adventure for Fifth Edition

Cartography by Jog Brogzin

Art by Matias Lazaro, Maciej Zagorski, and William McAusland

*This adventure is designed for three to seven 2nd- to 4th-level characters and is optimized for five characters with an average party level (APL) of 3. Characters outside this level range cannot participate in this adventure. The adventure takes place on the island of The Skeleton Key, first featured in the adventure **The Flight of the Predator** and then in the follow-up adventure **The Skeleton Key.** Both adventures may be found in BroadSword Monthly #5.*

This adventure can easily be placed on any remote island in a campaign setting of your choice.

Adventure Background

The Skeleton Key, a mysterious island hidden at the center of the Ocean of Warna, has just been rediscovered. The island is home to a tribe of warrior women named the Serpent Whisperers. They guard an ancient temple called the Temple of Grihoo. While they have sworn to protect the temple's secrets, none of the Whisperers actually know what lies within its lower levels.

The characters, having crash-landed on the island, find themselves at the mercy of these warrior women. In order to learn more about the island's secrets and/or find a way to escape the island, they will need to gain their trust.

Adventure Overview

The adventure's story is spread over nine parts. The entire adventure takes approximately 12 hours to play and will likely require multiple sessions. There are also three bonus sections that can change and/or extend the structure of the story.

- **The Serpent Whisperers**. The characters meet the Serpent Whisperers and discover the Temple of Grihoo and its surrounding village.
- **Part 1. Life Among the Serpent Whisperers.** Recognizing that escape from the island is not an

option, the characters must settle down with the Serpent Whisperers and work to build their trust.

- *Part 2. The Dying Light.* The characters' motives are called into question when the two pylons that protect the island cease to function. Hopefully the party can convince the Serpent Whisperers of their innocence

- *Part 3. Arrival.* A flying vehicle of some sort lands north of the village. The characters must travel with the Serpent Whisperers to the landing zone and confront the visitors.

- *Part 4. Sabotage!* Someone has damaged the Peregrine flyer, the characters' only way off the island. The characters must follow clues leading to the saboteur's identity. *Part 5. Vuda and Her Cats.* The characters follow the tracks to a cave in the woods where they find the Serpent Whisperer Vuda.

- *Part 6. Aegreyan Assault.* The characters discover the true identity of the attackers. Just as they are about to confront their newfound enemy, the island and the village come under attack by a force of warriors from the drakeblood nation of Aegreya. The party must defend the village against the Aegreyans.

- *Part 7. The Temple of Grihoo.* The characters must follow a dangerous villain into the depths of the forbidden Temple of Grihoo.

- *Part 8. Grihoo the Traveler.* The characters confront the villain at the bottom of the temple. There, they learn the temple's greatest secret and the reason for The Skeleton Key.

- *Addenda.* Further information concerning variant endings and possible optional subplots may be found in the Addenda following the conclusion of the adventure.

Adventure Hooks

The following plot hooks provide some possible ways for the characters to get

involved in this adventure. Most of the adventure assumes that the characters have played through the first two installments of the *Titan's Heir* adventure series, *The Flight of the Predator* and *The Skeleton Key.* However, there are options available for those who wish to use this adventure as the jumping-off point.

Titan's Heir Storyline. The adventurers were on board the Dinzer warblimp *The Predator* when it crashed. The details of this event were covered in *Titan's Heir Part 1: The Flight of the Predator.* Following the crash, they worked with the other survivors to live on the island.

Faction Agent (The Tip of the Spear). The Tip has discovered the location of the island and believe it might contain lost treasure. While traveling to the island, the characters' ship was destroyed in a storm. The characters find themselves washed up on the beaches of The Skeleton Key. Right away, they are confronted by the Serpent Whisperers.

Faction Agent (Secrets of the Righteous). The Dinzers have rediscovered a lost island in the center of the Ocean of Warna. They believe that it may be where the infamous Dinzer mage, Odon, disappeared close to 450 years ago. While traveling to the island, the characters' ship was destroyed in a storm. The characters

find themselves washed up the beach. Right away, they are confronted by the Serpent Whisperers.

Beginning the Adventure: The Serpent Whisperers

The characters happen upon (or are ushered to) the Temple of Grihoo and its surrounding village. For hundreds of years, the village has existed outside of the knowledge of even the most learned Omerian sages.

Read or paraphrase the following:

> The tree line breaks exposing a small village consisting of squat, expertly-built stone buildings. At the northern end of the village stands a huge stone temple measuring roughly 70 feet by 70 feet and standing 50 feet tall. The exterior walls are carved to look like hundreds of snakes crawling over top of each other. Two female human warriors wearing elaborate headdresses stand guard at the temple's entrance. Joining them are five muscular, 12-foot tall apes wearing bronze armor who climb over the sides of the building.
>
> At either side of the temple are two 200-foot tall obelisks made of steel. Roughly 10 feet from the top of each of these pylons there is a small window from which green light glows.

Area Description

While the Serpent Whisperer's village is detailed further in Appendix A, the village has the following basic features.

Dimensions & Terrain. The village itself consists of 14 buildings with flat rooves. The buildings are built of sandstone bricks. The majority of the buildings flank a narrow canal leading from the edge of the forest to the temple's steps.

Light. At night, the village is lit with torches. In addition, the pylons emit a dull green glow.

Pylons. The two pylons seemingly have no way to enter them. Should a character climb to the top and peer in the window, they will find a glowing, green rock similar to the one that powers *The Predator*. The pylons magically protect the island. Divination spells cannot find the island and teleportation magic does not work on the island, nor will it allow others outside the island to magically travel there. It also places an illusion over the island, making it invisible to those sailing past it. Those who've found the island in the past did so only by happenstance.

Serpent Whisperers. The village is home to over 30 Serpent Whisperers of Grihoo. The warrior women keep goats, chickens, and other livestock in the area. There are also **needleblast boas** (see Appendix D) that freely roam the village, offering additional protection where needed.

The Temple. The Temple of Grihoo is guarded by two Serpent Whisperer **Serpent Guards** and four **Heirs of Kong** (see Appendix D for details). The Serpent Guards are fanatical and will not turn from their posts, even in the presence of magic. The Temple is detailed further in Part 7 of this adventure.

Key to the Temple

Viothye has an unusual talisman hanging from her neck. It looks like a four-inch rectangular bit of twisted-steel with irregular edges and holes cut into it. A thin, glowing red line runs from each short edge to the other.

The talisman is not only a piece of jewelry, but it is actually the key that unlocks the many of the temple's doors (see Part 7 for details).

Creature Information

There are a few important NPCs for you to familiarize yourself with this adventure. The NPCs and village are detailed in Appendix A. However, if the characters openly enter the village and the Serpent Whisperers are aware of their presence, they are greeted by the village's leader, **Viothye** (see Appendix A).

What Does Viothye Want? Viothye is the village's elder and has held the role for close to twenty years. Her top priority is keeping the island and the temple a secret. She fundamentally believes that if the island and the Temple are discovered and fall into the wrong hands, doom would befall Casar.

When Viothye first meets the characters, she wishes to know their intentions. While sympathetic to their desire to leave the island, she can't allow them to do that. Viothye knows that warnings and threats will do little to curb the strong personalities of adventurers and instead gives them the choice. She explains:

> "There are choices that you can make to help us protect the island from those who would use its power for evil. And we could use those with your skills and talents to help us defend it."

The Serpent Whisperers possess no boats, and thanks to the pylons, there is no way to send messages off the island or travel via magic. Finally, the Serpent Whisperers would rather die than go against their strong beliefs.

What Does Viothye Know? If the characters have made their presence on the island obvious, she is already aware of their presence. She may even know their names and abilities (GM's discretion).

Viothye and her warriors have a few issues that they are trying to deal with when the characters arrive. Some of those issues they will ask the characters to help with. Others, she keeps quiet. Refer to Part 2 and Appendix A for potential side quests and downtime activities that the characters can participate in during their time with the Grihoo.

Viothye is also one of the few living Serpent Whisperers to know what lies below the top level of the Temple. She carries one of the keys to the temple around her neck (see the sidebar).

Live With Us

Viothye cannot let the characters escape. Even if the characters threaten her and her fellow warriors, she makes it clear that even if she did want to help them to escape, there was no way for them to do so.

"Even the Old Gods could not escape this island," she admonishes.

Once the characters understand that there is no easy escape from The Skeleton Key, Viothye makes an offer to build the characters (and any surviving NPCs from *The Predator*) a hut in which they can live. Furthermore, she will provide food, clothing, weapons, and anything else they need to help them in the beginning. Of course, she expects them to start earning their keep at some point.

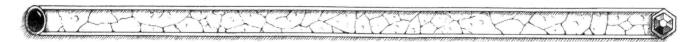

Part 1. Life Among the Serpent Whisperers

With no clear way to escape the island or send a message to people away from the island, the characters will have to learn to adjust to their new life among the Serpent Whispers.

Life on the Island

Although they are stranded on the island, the characters are still free to explore the island and get into adventures (see Appendix A for details on adventures and areas of exploration on the island). In addition, they can take downtime to keep themselves busy. Plus, they will need to earn the trust of the Serpent Whisperers, which will affect the outcome of the rest of the story.

Each week that the characters remain among the Serpent Whisperers they can perform downtime and "life on the island" tasks to improve their way of life. Plus, many of the activities will help them ingratiate themselves with the women warriors.

These downtime activities follow the same downtime rules identified in the *PHB* and *DMG*. Just as in *The Skeleton Key*, the character can undertake these activities on their own or they can task the other survivors of *The Predator* to help them. That way, the characters can focus on exploration and adventuring while their allies improve their stance with Viothye and the others.

Making a Downtime Check

When a "Life on the Island" task requires an ability check, one of the characters or one of their survivor allies can use their own ability check modifier to determine success. Three is the maximum number of NPCs that the players can use to perform these checks. You can address these scenes as a "montage" with quick descriptions of what transpired, or you can go a step further and create full scenes around the tasks. It's up to you and your players how you handle these.

Downtime and Life on the Island Activities

In addition to the activities found in other books, the characters and their fellow survivors can undertake the new activities presented in this section, either as regular activities or as "life on the island" tasks. Note that many of these activities replace the ones found in the second part of this adventure series, *The Skeleton Key*.

The length of time required to perform a task is typically one or more workweeks (a single workweek is 5 days). All the normal rules for downtime must be followed by the character or NPC survivor including spending 8 hours each day engaged in that activity for the day to count toward the activity's completion. Downtime activities often involve strenuous physical or mental activity. Therefore, a character or NPC cannot both perform downtime and adventure on the same day without suffering the effects of exhaustion.

Some of the downtime activities described in this Part affect the party's relationship with the Serpent Whisperers of Grihoo. See the "Earning Trust" section below for details on how earning the Serpent Whisperers' trust provides benefits (or even drawbacks) for the characters.

Help Viothye. There are a few tasks that Viothye needs help with but lacks the hands to perform. As the characters work to build trust with Viothye and the other Serpent Whisperers, they can request tasks from Viothye. Typically, Viothye expects a task to be completed in one week or less. Each time the characters succeed in performing a task for Viothye, they gain a cumulative +5 to their Earning Trust rolls at the end of the month.

The various tasks that the characters can perform are outlined in Appendix A.

Intelligence Gathering. The Serpent Whisperers hide many secrets on the island. The characters can spend their downtime trying to uncover some of those secrets.

Time Investment. Uncovering the secrets of the Serpent Whisperers requires at least one workweek of effort.

Resolution. The character declares the focus of the Intelligence Gathering using one of the following topics: the Island, Serpent Whisperers, or the Temple. Intelligence gathering requires three ability checks, reflecting the ongoing progress of uncovering the Serpent Whisperers' secrets. Any of the characters or their allies involved in the intelligence-gathering efforts can make a check. The abilities and skills applicable for each check are determined by the GM, reflecting the selected scheme and the ongoing narrative. For example, sneaking into the temple to see what's inside might require a Charisma (Persuasion) check to distract the guards, a Dexterity (Stealth) check to sneak into the temple itself, and a Wisdom (Perception) check to understand what is inside.

Because of the risks inherent in such activities, the DC for the check is determined randomly. The GM rolls 2d10+5 for the DC, generating a separate result for each check. The total number of successes determines the outcome of the activity, as noted in the Intelligence Gathering table.

Intelligence Gathering.

Result	Outcome
0 successes	You learn nothing.
1 success	You learn one secret.
2 successes	You learn two secrets.
3 successes	You learn three secrets.

Each secret available for the characters to learn are on the Secrets Learned sidebar. As the GM, you are the final arbiter concerning exactly what a character learns based on the skills they used to uncover the information.

Complications. Achieving 0 successes automatically generates a complication, but the GM may decide that a complication arises no matter what—especially if such a complication improves the story. The GM can choose a complication or roll on the Intelligence Gathering Complications table.

Intelligence Gathering Complications.

d6	Complication
1	One of the characters is caught by the Serpent Whisperers and severely punished. See Appendix A for a list of Serpent Whisperer punishments.
2	The characters are caught by a corrupt member of the Serpent Whisperers. She threatens to turn the characters in unless they meet her demands.
3	The characters left a clue that could reveal their intentions. One or more of the characters must try to cover up the clue before they are caught.
4	The characters learn a secret; unfortunately, the information is false.
5	The characters learn that an answer to a secret they seek is in a dangerous location. See Appendix A for details on possible locations for the secret.
6	The characters aren't the only ones who learn the secret. An ally, rival, or even a Serpent Whisperer learned the secret as well.

Earning Trust. Although Viothye has offered the characters and their fellow survivors a place to stay on the island, the Serpent Whisperers do not immediately trust the characters. And although The Serpent Whisperers are helpful at the start

Secrets Learned

The following secrets can be learned by the characters through successful Intelligence Gathering checks.

The Island. If the focus of the character's Intelligence Gathering check is the island itself, they can learn the following secrets:

- Shortly before the characters arrived, a pair of males from the Temple escaped into the forest. The males are important to the survival of the Serpent Whisperers and Viothye is determined that they be captured and returned.
- A thousand years ago, the island was home to a race of birdfolk named the Disciples of Ze. It is unknown what happened to the birdfolk but their temple can still be found in the mountains.
- Powerful magic hides the island from the outside world. The magic is powered by the two 200-foot pylons that flank the village.
- Great serpents emerge from holes in the ground all over the island. The serpents have no tails; some of the women believe that they are all part of one colossal being.
- There is a vicious race of beings that haunt the forest to the west. The Serpent Whisperers call them "Monster Men."

The Serpent Whisperers. If the focus of the character's Intelligence Gathering check is the Serpent Whisperers, they can learn the

following secrets:

- The original Serpent Whisperers came from an island across the ocean hundreds of years ago. They were the slaves of a dangerous race of fiends known as *danaavrakti*.
- The Serpent Whisperers propagate their kind by breeding with men. All of the men come from within the temple. Many of the Serpent Whisperers believe that the Temple—who some revere as a god—is a gift to them.
- Some of the Serpent Whisperers are born with a curse called *firemind*. Those who have firemind are prone to angry outbursts. Vuda, Ykyope's sister, is believed to have firemind.

The Temple. If the focus of the character's Intelligence Gathering check is the Temple, they can learn the following secrets:

- The Serpent Whisperers believe that there is a great treasure deep within the temple.
- Every few years, a man randomly emerges from the temple, disoriented. Although it's a new man each time, the men always look exactly the same. The Serpent Whisperers enslave these men.
- Anyone who enters the door at the rear of the temple vanishes. Only Viothye has a key to the door, which she wears around her neck.

of the relationship with the characters, unless the characters make efforts to ingratiate themselves with the Serpent Whisperers, the benefits provided by the Serpent Whisperers will start to fade.

Time Investment. Unless the GM decides otherwise, this task must be run at the end of each month that the characters spend on the island among the Serpent Whisperers. Unlike other activities, results are determined for Earning Trust even if specific characters and survivors are not allocated to the activity. However, allocating char-

acters and NPCs to the tasks greatly improves their chances for a favorable outcome. This allocation represents assisting the Serpent Whisperers with tasks, building rapport, and other tasks to shed a positive light on the group.

During any given month, the players decide how many days their characters and the other survivors can dedicate to this activity. As normal, characters and NPCs cannot perform other activities while focused on Earning Trust, and days spent adventuring or engaged in other activities cannot be used for this activity.

Resolution. Percentile dice are rolled by a player nominated for this task by the group. The number of total days spent by all characters and staff members on this activity are added to the roll. That total is then compared to the Earning Trust table to determine what happens for the month.

Benefits. Earning the Serpent Whisperers' trust grants the characters certain benefits which can help them survive throughout the week. Benefits can either be permanent or temporary. Temporary benefits last until the end of the month following the roll on the Earning Trust table. It's possible for characters to lose any benefits that they receive through misdeeds or complications (GM's discretion).

The characters can earn the following benefits:

- *Ally Favor.* One of the Serpent Whisperers owes the characters a favor which they can use before the end of the next month. The GM decides the nature of this favor. If this is chosen as a permanent benefit, the ally only offers one favor per month.
- *Assistance.* One of the Serpent Whisperers helps the characters with one of their tasks. The characters make one of the Life on the Island rolls with advantage. The advantage must be used before the end of the next month. If the characters choose this as a permanent benefit, they only receive the benefit once per month.
- *Building Trust.* The characters add +10 to their next Earning Trust role. The characters can take this benefit multiple times and its effects are cumulative.
- *Charmed.* With this benefit, all Charisma checks made when dealing with the Serpent Whisperers are made with advantage.
- *Secret.* One of the Serpent Whisperers shares a secret with the characters choosing from Secrets Learned on page 14. If this is a permanent benefit, the Serpent Whisperer only shares one secret per month.
- *Supplies.* The Serpent Whisperers give the characters and their NPC allies enough food and water to survive until the end of the next month.

Escape. Although Viothye warned the characters that it was impossible to escape the island, they may still try to discover a way to do so.

Time Investment. Gathering the appropriate information and resources requires at least two workweeks of effort.

The characters and their fellow survivors must also have access to resources like building materials in order to accomplish the task.

Resolution. Characters or survivors in charge of the escape attempt must make two ability checks with a DC of 14. First, a character or survivor must succeed at either an Intelligence check using proficiency in water vehicles to select the right vision or identify the best way to escape the island. This check gains a +1 bonus for every character or NPC that has the sailor background (use your discretion for the NPCs).

A character or survivor must then make a Charisma (Deception or Persuasion) check to ensure that the Serpent Whisperers (at least those who aren't their allies) don't notice their efforts. This check gains a +1 bonus if the character or NPC has the charlatan or criminal background.

All checks gain a +1 bonus for every two workweeks beyond the initial time that is spent undertaking this activity. A maximum bonus of +10 can be applied to each check.

The total number of successes determines the outcome of the activity, as noted on the Escape table.

Earning Trust.

d100 + Days	Result
10 or less	The Serpent Whisperers lose all faith in the characters. The characters can no longer stay in the village and must live out in the forests until they can earn their trust. Unless the characters do something that proves their value to the Serpent Whisperers, the Serpent Whisperers act hostile towards them in all future encounters. The characters can surrender a previously earned benefit or inspiration to ignore this result. See Appendix A for details.
11-25	The Serpent Whisperers do not trust the characters, but allow them to remain in the village regardless. The characters gain no benefits.
26-50	The Serpent Whisperers do not fully trust the characters, but offer to help them a little. The characters gain one temporary benefit.
51-75	The Serpent Whisperers start to trust the characters somewhat. The characters gain two temporary benefits.
76-98	The characters gain the trust of the Serpent Whisperers for the month. They gain one permanent benefit and two temporary benefits.
99+	The characters earn the full trust of the Serpent Whisperers. They permanently gain all of the benefits of the Serpent Whisperers. Unless the characters do something that breaks the Serpent Whisperers' trust, they no longer have to roll to Earn Trust.

Escape Table.

Result	Outcome
0 successes	The characters make no progress.
1 success	The characters make progress on their escape plan. The next time the characters take the Escape task, they make their checks with advantage.
2 successes	The characters create a solid plan for escape. Now, they must put it into action. See Appendix A for details on potential Escape Plans.

Complications. A result of 0 successes typically indicates that the failed escape results in a complication. At the GM's discretion, even a successful outcome might have unexpected side effects. The GM can choose a complication or roll on the Escape Complications table.

Escape Complications.

d4	Complication
1	One of the characters is caught by the Serpent Whisperers and severely punished. See Appendix A for a list of Serpent Whisperer punishments.
2	The characters are caught by a corrupt member of the Serpent Whisperers. She threatens to turn the characters in unless they meet her demands.
3	The characters left a clue that could reveal their intentions. One or more of the characters must try to cover up the clue before they are caught.
4	The characters experience a major setback. The next time they perform the Escape task, the time investment is four weeks instead of two.

Explore the Island. The characters can search the island in real time as described in *The Skeleton Key* and the Island Exploration section in Appendix A.

Time Investment. Exploring a portion of The Skeleton Key requires at least one workweek of effort. Spending more time increases the chance that the expedition finds something of use.

Resolution. A character or survivor directing the expedition makes a Wisdom (Survival) check to determine the outcome. This check gains a +1 bonus for each workweek beyond the first that is spent exploring. A maximum bonus of +10 can be applied to this check. The total of the check determines the outcome, as shown on the Explore the Island table.

Explore the Island.

Check Total	Discovery
1-5	Major threat
6-10	Minor threat
11-25	No discovery of note
26+	Secret location

Major Threat. A result on the table indicating a major threat represents a discovery, event, or other entity that might endanger the characters and potentially the entire island. See Appendix A for examples.

Minor Threat. A minor threat to the charactres involves uncovering a danger that can disrupt the characters' ability to earn the trust of the Serpent Whisperers along with their livelihoods. See Island Exploration in Appendix A for examples.

Secret location. The island is full of strange and important locations for the characters to uncover. Examples of locations are included in the Island Exploration section of Appendix A.

Complications. A result of 1-10 on the Explore the Island table is its own complication, but the GM can add unexpected side effects to a successful result choosing from or rolling on the Explore the Island Complications table.

Explore the Island Complications.

d6	Complication
1	The same time that the characters discover something on the island, the Serpent Whisperers or another rival also discover it.
2	One of the characters' NPC allies goes missing during the exploration activity. Their fate is a mystery that the characters must resolve.
3	The location that the characters discover is cursed. The party becomes lost for one day.
4	The next time the characters return to the location it is missing; either they cannot find it again or it has simply vanished through mysterious circumstances.
5	The characters' discovery has drawn the attention of a dangerous creature on the island. Choose or roll randomly on the major or minor threats tables in Appendix A, Island Exploration.
6	Following the discovery, the characters start to experience all sorts of bad omens.

Part 2. The Dying Light

As the characters adjust to their new life on the island, something happens that causes a stir among the Serpent Whisperers. Depending on the trust the characters have built among the Serpent Whisperers, they may need to defend themselves and their actions from the warrior women or suffer severe consequences.

Screams in the Night

So long as the characters are still among the Serpent Whisperers, after 2d6 weeks of living with the warrior women, they are woken to the sound of screaming in the middle of the night.

Should the characters investigate, they discover that the commotion comes from all of the Serpent Whisperers standing outside staring up at the pylons.

> On any other night, the pylons give off a dull green glow. But tonight, there's nothing. Just darkness.
>
> From behind you, someone shouts in broken Common: "You! You did this! You kill the light! Now you make big trouble for us!"

Whoever accused the characters of killing the light is up to you. It can be someone random or an NPC detailed in Appendix A's "Grihoo Village."

Proving Innocence

Right away, the Serpent Whisperers take the dying light as a dreadful omen. After all, things were fine before the characters and the other survivors of *The Predator* showed up—now the light from the pylons are out.

The characters must argue their case before the warrior women. Have the players make their arguments. Then, have them make a group DC 15 Charisma (Persuasion) check. Additionally, all survivor NPCs make a single check, a d20 roll plus the highest Charisma modifier among the characters. Each character gains a bonus to his or her check based on

the group's current level of trust (see Earning Trust in Part 1). Don't forget to add in any benefits from successful Earning Trust checks.

Determine how many of the group's checks succeeds—the characters' and the NPC's—then consult the Proving Innocence table.

- A total success occurs if all checks are successful
- A success occurs if half or more checks are successful
- A failure occurs if less than half the checks are successful
- A total failure occurs if all checks fail.

Proving Innocence Table.

Result	Outcome
Total Failure	The characters are exiled from the village. See Grihoo Village in Appendix A for details on Exile.
Failure	One of the characters must suffer punishment at the hands of the Serpent Whisperers. Once they do, they are free of further consequences. See Appendix A for Serpent Whisperer Punishments.
Success	The characters prove their innocence but suffer a -10 penalty to their next Earning Trust check.
Total Success	The characters prove their innocence and suffer no consequences.

Part 3. Arrival

The island is visited by a group from the mainland led by a wealthy Pressonian noble named Theo Barbakis. As long as the characters are free and still living among the Serpent Whisperers, they are asked to greet the Pressonians and learn as much as they can about the visitors.

Trouble

A few weeks (2d6) after the pylons stop glowing, the Serpent Whisperers spot a flying vehicle of some sort a few miles north of the village. So long as the characters have not been imprisoned by the Serpent Whisperers following the events of Part 2 and they have earned at least some modicum of trust (they do not suffer a penalty to their Charisma checks when dealing with the Serpent Whisperers), Viothye tasks the characters to join a squad of six **amazon warriors** lead by Ykyope (LN female human **amazon warrior** with 55 hit points) who wields a *brutal macuahuitl*. See Appendix C for details.

The Peregrine

A large, steel vehicle shaped like a bird has landed in a clearing roughly four miles north of the village. When the characters, Ykyope, and the other Serpent Whisperers arrive, already, the ship's crew and passengers are unloading equipment.

The flying vehicle is a **Dinzer peregrine-class flyer** (see Appendix C) named *Three Hands Down*. It is owned by a Pressonian noble named **Theofilos Barbakis** who is among the passengers. Joining Barbakis are a dragonborn Pressonian warrior named **Qiu Xiang**, a pair of devilkin sorcerer siblings named **Rain in the Moonlight** and **Vision of the Water**, and a wanderer halfling named **Yarry**.

Area Description

The clearing has the following features.

Dimensions & Terrain. The clearing sits on a cliff overlooking the island's coastline 100-feet below. The grass here is tall, and depending on the season, there may be plenty of wildflowers, too. The tree line in which the characters and the Serpent Whisperers hide is approximately 150 feet from *Three Hands Down*. The cliff's name is the Cliff of Eyes.

Light. The Serpent Whisperers are humans, therefore, they prefer to approach during the day.

Supply Crates. The passengers of *Three Hands Down* have started to unload large crates into the clearing in order to set up camp. If combat breaks out, the passengers can use the crates as cover.

Windy. The wind coming off the water of the Ocean of Warna blasts the clearing. Although it's not strong enough to affect ranged combat or flyers, it does make hearing difficult. All creatures in the clearing have a -5 to Wisdom (Perception) checks that rely on hearing.

Battle!

The Serpent Whisperers are easily rattled and the presence of Barbakis and his crew are enough to put them on edge. A passive Wisdom (Insight) check of 15 or better reveals that Ykyope would rather attack first and ask questions later. Unless one of the characters uses their action to try and calm Ykyope and the other Serpent Whisperers down with a contested Charisma (Persuasion) check contested by Ykyope's Wisdom (Insight) check, Ykyope shouts a war cry and charges.

Barbakis stays out of the fight; he runs onto the ship and hides. Meanwhile, the other four take cover and prepare to defend themselves against the Serpent Whisperers. It should be obvious to the characters that Barbakis' crew are much better armed and equipped than the Serpent Whisperers.

The statistics for Barbakis and his crew are included in Appendix A.

The Peregrine Crew vs The Serpent Whisperers: Simplified

You can run this battle the typical way, or you can abstract the actions of the NPCs to make combat run smoother with more focus on the characters' actions. If you do, instead of determining the actions for each of the NPCs involved, refer to the Peregrine Crew vs The Serpent Whisperers table to determine their actions.

Each of the crew of the Peregrine have their own initiative count and actions, as does Ykyope. The other Serpent Whisperers, on the other hand, act as one.

On an NPC's initiative count (losing initiative ties), instead of choosing actions and rolling dice for the NPC, roll a d20 to determine what happens during that NPC's turn. If an NPC is incapacitated, skip their turn. If an NPC suffers a wound, it makes its d20 roll with disadvantage. And if an NPC is in direct conflict with a character, decide and roll their actions as normal.

Trembling with fear, Barbakis stays out of the fight and hides on the ship until the combat is over.

Resolution

At some point, the characters should intervene. If the characters don't intervene, one of Barbakis' crew (likely Qiu Xiang) tries to stop the fight, especially after one or more of the Serpent Whisperers are injured.

Once things have calmed down a little, Barbakis reemerges and tries to introduce himself.

Creature Information

Barbakis and his crew understand why the Serpent Whisperers attack and don't blame them. They quickly explain what they are doing on the island.

What Do They Want? Barbakis explains that a few months ago (right around the time the pylons stopped glowing) a major event happened on the mainland that caused strange effects all over the world. Barbakis, a historian and museum curator, had been looking for a Pressonian relic for years but was unable to find it. The relic was a 400-year old sword owned by a Pressonian knight named Gozwik. (The sword included in *The Skeleton Key*.)

While Gozwik was beloved, the true reason that Barbakis was searching for Gozwik's sword was not to find the knight, but the person who the knight was supposed to be traveling with: the Dinzer Odon, founder of Odonburg. Gozwik and Odon vanished four centuries ago somewhere in the Ocean of Warna and no one has been able to find their final resting place. Barbakis believes that the pair found the island and disappeared. But the island's magic kept them from being discovered. Until now.

Barbakis promises the characters that if they can help him find the location of Gozwik's sword as well as the final resting place of the Dinzer Odon, he will not only give them a ride back to the mainland in the Peregrine but pay them 500 gp each for their efforts.

The four members of Barbakis' crew are only interested in the payment they will receive from Barbakis once they help Barbakis find what he is looking for.

What Do They Know? Barbakis comes off as aloof, cowardly, and physically weak—he's incredibly out of shape. However, his thirst for knowledge and the glory that would come with finding the final resting place of the Dinzer Odon is enough to make him ignore his troubles.

Barbakis' crew knows very little about Barbakis. All four were part of an adventuring party from The Summer Land who were hired by Barbakis to travel to the island. Overall, they trust Barbakis enough to journey with him to The Skeleton Key but know nothing beyond what Barbakis shares with the characters.

Even if they are invited back to the Serpent Whisperers' village, Barbakis and his crew prefer to set up camp and remain near *Three Hands Down*.

Peregrine Crew vs The Serpent Whisperers.

Outcome	Peregrine Crew	Serpent Whisperers
The NPC attacks and misses its intended target.	1-8	1-12
The NPC wounds its intended target. Roll a d20 and refer to the Random NPC table below to determine who was wounded.	9-18	13-20
The NPC incapacitates its intended target. Roll a d20 and refer to the Random NPC table below to determine who was incapacitated.	20	—

Random NPC (d20).

NPC	Peregrine Crew	Serpent Whisperers
Qiu Xiang	—	1-5
Rain in the Moonlight	—	6-10
Vision on the Water	—	11-15
Yarry	—	16-20
Ykopye	1-2	—
1 **amazon warrior**	3-18	—
2 **amazon warriors**	19-20	—

Part 4. Sabotage

Someone has ransacked Barbakis' ship and disabled its engine! Distraught, Barbakis asks the characters to discover who destroyed their ship while they work to repair it. He offers a healthy gold reward if the characters can discover who did it. A set of tracks leads from the ship to a cave near the mountains.

"I Can't Stand It!"

After a few weeks (1d4) working alongside Barbakis and his crew, Barbakis sends word to the characters that he needs their help.

If the characters agree and travel back to the clearing, they find Barbakis distraught. He leads them inside the flyer and into the engine room. The only one of Barbakis' crew with him is the halfling, Yarry. The other three are scouring the island for clues leading to Gozwin and Odon's final resting place.

Read:

> Claws marks! They're everywhere, too, almost as if some sort of wild cat attacked the engine room. Not only are the walls and components scratched, but various cables running towards a pedestal at the center of the room have been torn away. The ends of the cable ooze a strange, light green liquid onto the floor.
>
> "The entire engine has been sabotaged! Not only that, but
>
> they've stolen the emerald odonburgite core *that powers the ship*. Even if we could repair this mess, without the core, we can't possibly get anywhere!"
>
> Barbakis paces back and forth biting his nails. He looks on the edge of tears.
>
> "This is sabotage. I can't stand it—I must know who planned it!"

If asked if he has any other methods of getting off the island, Barbakis remembers that there is a *sending stone* in the cockpit. Unfortunately, it appears that the stone has been stolen, too.

Barbakis implores that the characters discover who did it. If the characters are reluctant, he offers to double the reward, reminding them that without the Odonburgite core, they will all be stuck there.

Yarry offers to accompany the characters.

Tracks

Right away, the character with the highest passive (Wisdom) Perception check notices that there are tracks leading away from the ship. The tracks appear to be one set of humanoid prints joined by two sets of large cat (**tiger**) prints.

The characters can follow the tracks with a successful DC 15 Wisdom (Survival) check. If the characters are unable to successfully follow the tracks, Yarry can act as tracker instead.

The tracks take the characters nearly 20 miles into the wilderness to the mouth of a cave.

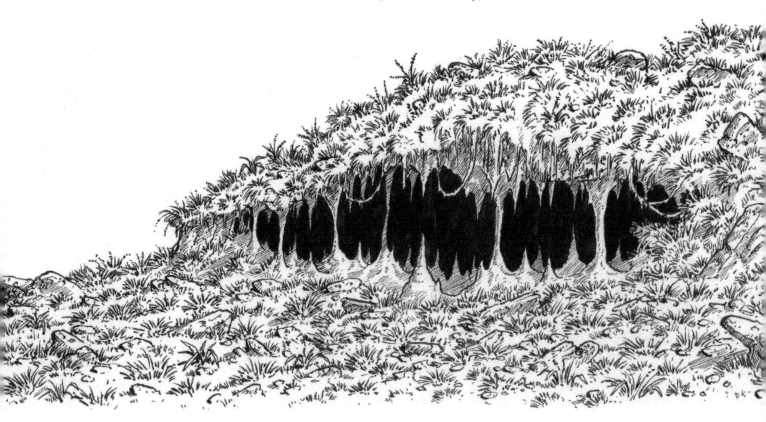

Part 5. Vuda and Her Cats

The characters discover Vuda inside the cave with the *emerald odonburgite* core. The moment that she notices the characters, she attacks. The characters must convince her they are innocent or defeat her in combat.

The Cave

When the characters find the cave, read or paraphrase the following:

> Before you lies the mouth of a cavern. The tracks you were following vanish into the darkness beyond.

If Yarry is still traveling with the characters he steps forward with his bow drawn. "It's likely a trap," he warns.

Eventually, the sound of a tiger roaring comes from within, signs that someone might be in there.

Area Description

The cave has the following features:

Dimensions & Terrain. The mouth of the cave itself is 10-feet wide and 7-feet high. The ground leading into the cave starts to descend at a 50-degree angle starting at the mouth. Forest creepers spill into the cave, creating easy handholds for the characters and Yarry to descend. Inside, the cavern is no larger than 20 feet by 20 feet. Vuda lies on the ground next to a glowing-green bag.

Emerald Odonburgite. The *emerald odonburgite* (see Appendix C) core of *Three Hands Down* is stowed in Vuda's leather satchel.

Tigers. Vuda's two **tigers** flank her on either side, guarding her. They snarl at the characters as they enter.

Creature Description

When the characters arrive the tigers stand and growl. Eventually, the noise is enough to wake Vuda. Vuda (CN **amazon warrior**) (see Appendix D) seems incredibly disoriented and exhausted (she has one level of exhaustion due to lack of sleep).

Confused, she draws her weapon and attacks.

What Does Vuda Know? If the characters manage to stop Vuda without killing her, Vuda shares with them that the last thing she remembers was being attacked by some sort of creature in the dark that scratched her on her back. Her tigers tried to fight it, but their claws did nothing against whatever it was. Before she could escape, the thing grabbed her, handed her the satchel, and told her to "hide this far from here." No matter how hard she tried to fight it, she was compelled to follow the instructions. She traveled for eight hours straight until she discovered the cave. Exhausted from the march she collapsed right where the characters found her. She also remembers that no matter how hard she tried to sleep, she was plagued by nightmares.

> "It was some sort of creature. Like a tiger—but different. Red mist escaped from its mouth, and its fur moved around it like snakes. No matter where I ran in my dream, I could not escape the beast.'"

What Happened to Vuda? A character who succeeds on a DC 12 Intelligence (Arcana) check immediately recognizes that Vuda was placed under the effects of an enchantment spell, likely *suggestion*. Furthermore, a character who succeeds on a DC 17 Intelligence (History or Religion) check may realize that the creature she described was a danaavrakt (**rakshasa**), a fiend whose very touch can bestow a curse that robs its victim of sleep. A *remove curse* spell or similar magic cures Vuda of her ailment.

Explosion and Cave-in

Just as the characters are about to leave, an explosion occurs at the mouth of the cave. Each character within 10 feet of the cave mouth must make a DC 13 Dexterity saving throw. A character takes 14 (4d6) fire damage from the blast on a failed saving throw or half as much damage on a successful one.

To make matters worse, the front of the cave collapses, trapping the characters, Vuda, and Yarry within.

The characters will have to use magical means to escape the cave or they will have to spend 8 hours digging their way out. The time spent moving the boulders is exhausting; treat the effort as if the characters had spent the day traveling. If the characters don't take a long rest after escaping the cave, at the end of each hour that they spend traveling or performing strenuous activities (including combat) they must make a Constitution saving throw. The DC is 10 + 1 for each hour past the time it took for them to escape. On a failed saving throw, a character suffers one level of exhaustion.

If the characters discovered another creative method of escaping the cavern, you can ignore this rule.

Clues to the Attackers

Outside of the cave, the characters find a two pairs of footprints in addition to their own. In addition, they discover a strong-smelling yellow powder sprinkled on the ground along with animal pellets. A character who succeeds on a DC 13 Intelligence (Arcana) check recognizes that the powder is sulfur and the pellets are bat guano; it's the components for a *fireball* spell.

Any character who succeeds on a DC 15 Intelligence (Survival) check can draw the conclusion that the footprints belong to Rain in the Moonlight and Vision of the Water. If Yarry is with the group, the characters may immediately start throwing blame his way. However, Yarry is innocent; like the characters, he hasn't known the devilkin brother and sister for very long. They were all hired separately.

Part 6. Aegreyan Assault

After the characters escape the cave-in, they discover that an Aegreyan battalion is attacking the island. The characters must team with the Serpent Whisperers to repel their forces. Meanwhile, Barbakis steals Viothye's key and enters the Temple.

Back to the Clearing

If the characters return to the clearing, they discover that the flyer has been abandoned. Barbakis, the devilkin, and Qiu Xiang are gone. Fresh tracks reveal that they headed back towards the village.

Anything of value in the flyer has been stripped. Furthermore, it appears that there have been no efforts made to repair the engine. It's almost as if they planned to abandon it in the first place.

"Look!"

The character with the highest passive Wisdom (Perception) check is the first to notice something a mile off the coast. There appears to be a large bird flying toward the island. After watching for a moment, it quickly becomes apparent that it's not a bird—it's a dragon. A **young red dragon** to be precise.

Once the characters can make out the size and shape of the dragon, they recognize that the dragon isn't alone. Joining the dragon are 15 **griffon**-mounted Aegreyan elites (**half-red dragon veterans**). They carry the winged-serpent banners of Aegreya, the Isle of Dragons.

As long as the characters don't draw too much attention to themselves, the dragon and griffon-riders pass overhead without attacking them. Their target is the village and the Temple of Grihoo.

The village is four miles from the clearing. At a fast pace, the characters can reach the village in an hour. Unfortunately, it will take the dragon and griffon riders only 20 minutes to get there. The characters will know when the dragon and griffon riders reach the village as they will hear the sounds of the Serpent Whisperers' war drums and battle cries in the distance.

The Assault

By the time the characters arrive, the Aegreyans will have already laid waste to most of the village.

Area Description

Following the Aegreyan's assault, the village has the following features:

Bodies. Bodies from both sides litter the battlefield. Sadly, the majority of the bodies are dead Serpent Whisperers, killed by the Aegreyans and their dragon.

Burning Huts. All of the Serpent Whisperers' homes lie in ruin, burned to a crisp by the red dragon's breath. Notably, the bodies of the Serpent Guard and the Heirs of Kong lie at the base of the temple's steps, dead.

The Temple. After the characters assess the scene, read the following:

> At the top of the temple's steps just in front of the entrance, you see Barbakis—he holds Viothye by her neck. Desperately,
> she attacks him with her staff; the weapon doesn't seem to affect him. Barbakis tears the amulet from her neck then tosses her aside. Viothye rolls to the bottom of the steps, landing in the mud below—she's not moving.
> Barbakis stares back at you. For a brief moment, his eyes appear yellow—almost like a cat's eyes. He sneers as he spins on his heel and enters the temple.

Before the characters can react, the devilkin siblings **Rain in the Moonlight** and **Vision of the Water** step in the characters' path, blocking the way to the temple. Having already failed once in stopping the characters, the pair are determined not to fail a second time. See Appendix A for their stats.

Combat with Rain and Vision

The devilkin siblings Rain and Vision are focused on fighting the characters. Their statistics are included in the Dramatis Personae section of this adventure. As the characters fight, the Aegreyans and their dragon continue to battle the surviving Serpent Whisperers.

Instead of rolling for the NPCs who are not in direct conflict with the characters, instead, treat the battle raging around the characters as a series of hazards and complications that they must overcome in addition to the siblings.

At the end of each of the combat's participant's turns, roll a d100. Consult the Combat Complications table to determine whether a complication occurs. If it does, it affects the next battle participant in the combat, not the participant who rolled the die. The participant who rolled the die or the participant affected by the complication can spend inspiration to negate the complication.

Although Rain and Vision are loyal to Barbakis, they also value their own lives. If either of the devilkin's hit points are reduced by half, the pair break from combat and flee. However, if one or the other is killed in combat, the surviving sibling goes into a reckless rage that lasts the remainder of the combat; while raging, the surviving sibling has advantage on attack rolls.

The Dragon

Just as the characters defeat the siblings, they are confronted by the Aegreyan's dragon. The dragon lands at the steps of the temple, blocking the entrance. The **young red dragon** has already taken considerable damage and is down to 99 hit points. It's also used its fire breath recently, so it will need to recharge before the dragon can use it again.

Although the characters will have to defeat the dragon to get into the

Combat Complications.

d100	Complication
01-6	A large, flaming obstacle such as a cart, burning timber, or collapsing wall falls in the character's way. Make a DC 15 Dexterity saving throw to avoid the obstacle. On a failed check, the character takes 7 (2d6) fire damage.
7-12	An **amazon warrior*** battling a **half-red dragon veteran** steps onto the battlefield; they both aren't watching where they're going. The participant must make a DC 15 Dexterity (Athletics) check to avoid them. On a failed check, the character can't take reactions until the start of their next turn and their movement speed is reduced by 10 feet.
13-14	The **young red dragon** flies overhead, breathing its fire onto the battlefield with the participant at the center of the blast. The participant and each creature within 10 feet of the character must succeed on a DC 17 Dexterity saving throw, taking 56 (16d6) fire damage on a failed saving throw or half as much damage on a successful one.
15-19	Two **half-red dragon veterans** join the siblings in the combat. They have only have 30 hit points each.
20-26	1d4 **amazon warriors*** join the characters in the combat against the siblings. They only have 10 hit points remaining each.
27-30	An **Heir of Kong*** appears and attacks the siblings.
31-32	One of the pylons loses its structural integrity and collapses directly in the path of the participant. Draw a 200-foot line that is 20-feet wide from the base of the pylon passing through the participant. Each creature in the area must succeed on a DC 15 Dexterity saving throw. On a successful saving throw, the target moves to the outside of where the pylon falls. If the target can't or won't move, it suffers the same effects as if it had failed its saving throw. On a failed saving throw, a creature takes 75 (20d6) bludgeoning damage and is restrained by rubble (escape DC 20). While restrained, the creature is prone. This can only happen once. Reroll any repeat results.
33-40	A random arrow hits the participant. The participant takes 3 (1d8) piercing damage.
41-00	No complication

*see Appendix D for creature statistics

temple, they are not alone.

Here To Help

Joining the characters' sides are a handful of surviving Serpent Whisperers—five **amazon warriors** (see Appendix D). These amazon warriors can be Ykyope, Vuda, or any other important Serpent Whisperers (GM's discretion). If the characters are low on hit points and resources, the Serpent Whisperers can run interference while the characters get inside the temple.

Aegreyan Warriors

Once the characters defeat the dragon, more Aegreyans show up. Any surviving Serpent Whisperers encourage the characters to head into the temple while they hold off the Aegreyans.

Vioythe

When the characters reach Viothye, she's fading fast. Before she dies, she whispers to one character: "Find the *flail*. It's the only thing that can control Grihoo."

Part 7. The Temple of Grihoo

Hot on the heels of Barbakis—whatever he actually is—the characters enter the Temple of Grihoo.

Area Description

Unless otherwise stated, the Temple of Grihoo has the following features.

Dimensions & Terrain. The temple is carved out of an unfamiliar smoke-colored stone resembling polished marble. The floor tiles are colored differently from room to room, laid out in twisted mosaics and jagged patterns. Most of the rooms in the temple have 15-foot high ceilings.

Doors. The doors are fashioned from unique, green wood unlike any found anywhere else in the world. The doors have AC 15, 5 hp, and immunity to poison and psychic damage. When locked, the door can be broken open with a successful DC 15 Strength (Athletics) check or the lock can be picked with a successful DC 15 Dexterity check using proficiency in thieves' tools.

Elevators. There are two elevators in the complex. The first elevator, E1, connects Level 0 to Level 2 and 3. The second elevator, E2, connects Level 3 to Level 4.

Light. The first floor has torches placed into sconces throughout. The remainder of the temple has its own light sources.

Magical Defenses. Transportive spells such as *teleport*, *gate*, and *dimension door* (and items and features which duplicate their effects) do not function if used to move individual objects into or out of the temple. These spells function normally if employed within the confines of the temple. Astral and ethereal characters may enter the structure, however, and *portable holes* and *bags of holding* operate normally. The temple is protected against *scrying* (*crystal balls*, *clairvoyance* spells, and the like) and is magically protected against a spell that might be used to damage it (such as *disintegrate*).

The ranges of all divination-type spells cast (or similar effects) within the temple are restricted to the room or corridor in which the spell is cast. Peering into other planes from within the temple is not possible, except within certain areas as noted. The temple cannot be spied on from any source external to it except where noted otherwise.

Sounds. There is a slight hum heard throughout the temple that grows louder the deeper the characters descend.

Well (W). The entire complex is connected by a large, 15-foot diameter well that starts at Level 0 and ends in the ceiling above Level 4. The well's shaft is not open to Levels 1 through 3.

Level 0 - Ground Level

The surface level of the temple shares the same motif as the Serpent Whisperers' village. Although it's difficult to tell, the temple looks hundreds of years old.

0.01 - Entrance

There is no door blocking the entrance to the temple. Dried palm fronds blown in from the confrontation outside litter the front dais and entry.

0.02 - Main Hall

The bulk of the first floor is dominated by this main hall.

Area Description. This area has the following features:

Elevator E1. Behind the throne is a smooth panel of the wall. Carved into the wall beside this panel there is an embossed depiction of a multi-headed serpent. Waving Vioythe's key (or any other key like it) in front of the serpent temporarily "melts" the wall panel away, revealing a 10 x 10 room behind it—an elevator (E1). There are only two buttons on the control panel: up and down. If the characters press down, a quick, 6-second ride places the characters in **area 2.17** on Level 2.

Pillars. Eight massive pillars organized around the well prop up the ceiling.

Stairs (East). The eastern staircase descends 25 feet down to **area 1.01**.

Stairs (West). The western staircase descends 25 feet down to **area 1.02**.

Throne. At the northernmost end of the room stands a large throne made from the same smoke-colored stone. Carved onto the throne is the statue of a multi-headed serpent, a hydra.

Well (W). A huge, 15-foot diameter well is at the center of the room. The lip of the well is only a few inches off the ground. A quick glance down reveals that it goes up to 100-feet into the ground. Creatures that can see in the dark can see that it ends in a pool of water at the very bottom. At all times, the well gives off a subtle necrotic exhaust. Whenever a creature starts its turn in the well it must make a DC 15 Constitution saving throw. A creature takes 27 (6d8) necrotic damage on a failed saving throw or half as much damage on a successful one.

0.03 - Chamber of Heroes

The walls of this chamber are painted with a centuries-old mural depicting a band of heroes. What's unusual, each of the heroes roughly looks like one of the characters. Give rough descriptions of each of the drawings with one or two characteristics that match the characters. Finally, one of the characters (GM's discretion) is holding a multi-headed flail—an item that the character is unlikely to possess when this area is first discovered.

0.04 - Chamber of the Traveler

The walls of this chamber are painted with a centuries-old mural depicting the Heir of Grihoo holding the *hydra flail* (see **0.03**). The hero stands before a multi-headed snake—a hydra. On

a mural on the connecting wall, the hero and the hydra are standing in front of some sort of portal.

0.05 - Chamber of the Destructor

The walls of this chamber are painted with a centuries-old mural depicting one hundred children. All of the children look exactly the same except for one of the children who has blank eyes. Noticing the difference requires a successful DC 15 Wisdom (Perception) check.

Furthermore, the children are arranged in such a way that they take on the rough shape of the continent of Omeria. The child with blank eyes is placed on the eastern edge of Omeria. A character who succeeds on a DC 13 Intelligence (History) check recognizes that the blank-eyed child is placed approximately near the city of Naqqad.

0.06 - Chamber of Titans

The walls of this chamber are painted with a centuries-old mural depicting twelve unusual creatures. The twelve creatures are as follows:

- A turtle
- A horned beast
- A multi-headed serpent
- An owl
- A frog with four eyes
- A worm
- An elk
- A two-headed mantis
- A spider
- A skeleton wearing a crown
- An eagle
- A squid

The creatures are evenly spaced apart and facing forward. Whichever character was depicted in the mural in **area 0.03** gets a chill down their spine when they see the multi-headed serpent. Whenever they aren't facing the mural, they think they can see the heads turning to look toward them out of the corner of their eye. When they turn their head, the serpent returns to normal. No one else notices this phenomenon.

0.07 - Chamber of the Serpent

The walls of this chamber are painted with a centuries-old mural depicting a strange-looking diagram. A player's handout copy of the diagram is included in Appendix E. The diagram actually shows where the stone idol in the Cubby Room (**area 1.10**) is located.

0.08. - Chamber of the Temple

The walls of this chamber are painted with a centuries-old mural that reveals a map of the complex. A player's handout copy of the map is included in Appendix E.

0.09 - Chamber of the Danaavrakts

The walls of this chamber are painted with a centuries-old mural depicting a dozen tiger-headed humanoids. The thumbs on their hands are reversed. They are surrounding what-looks-like a glowing child with blank eyes. The child looks exactly like the one in **area 0.05**.

0.10 - Chamber of the Elves

The walls of this chamber painted with a centuries-old mural depicting what-looks-like elves. There are twelve different elves. One of the elves, a female, is holding a weapon that looks like a glaive. Another is holding a large, jagged-looking greatsword. Elven characters who enter this room feel a chill go down their spine.

0.11 - Healing Pool

A massive, shallow pool dominates this room. The pool has a slight, blue glow to it.

Healing Pool. The pool heals creature that enter its waters The first time a creature enters the pool and at the start of the creature's turn, it heals 10 hit points. After the pool has restored a total of 100 hit points to one or more creatures, it cannot restore any more hit points until 24 hours have passed. The pool has no effect on undead and constructs.

Level 1 - First Sub-Level

Right away, the characters will notice that there is something different about this level. Although the temple still looks hundreds of years old, there are marks and designs on the wall unlike anything the character have ever seen.

Power Grid

When the characters first set foot on this level, the power grid is down. There are no lights throughout the complex and many of the features and traps will not work unless the power grid is on. The only way to turn the power grid on is by pushing the boulder into place in **area 1.09**.

1.01 - East Landing

The stairs here lead back up to the eastern staircase in **area 0.02**.

Beams of Light. When the characters first come into this level of the temple, the power grid is off. The way into **area 1.09** is open. However, once the power grid comes back on, beams of light block passage to **area 1.09**. A creature that touches the beams takes 7 (2d6) lightning damage. A character can make a DC 13 Intelligence (Arcana) check to determine how the bars work. Then the same character can disable the bars with a successful DC 15 Dexterity check using proficiency in thieves' tools.

Secret Door. When the floor panel in **area 1.09** is pressed, it opens up the secret door in the southern wall. When the door is closed, a successful DC 11 Wisdom (Perception) recognizes it for what it is. A character can use his or her action to pry open the door with a successful DC 17 Strength (Athletics) check.

1.02 - Eastern Passage

The eastern passage connects **areas 1.01, 1.03, 1.05,** and **1.11**.

Area Description. The area has the following features.

Pillars. Three large, 5-foot thick marble pillars hold the ceiling aloft.

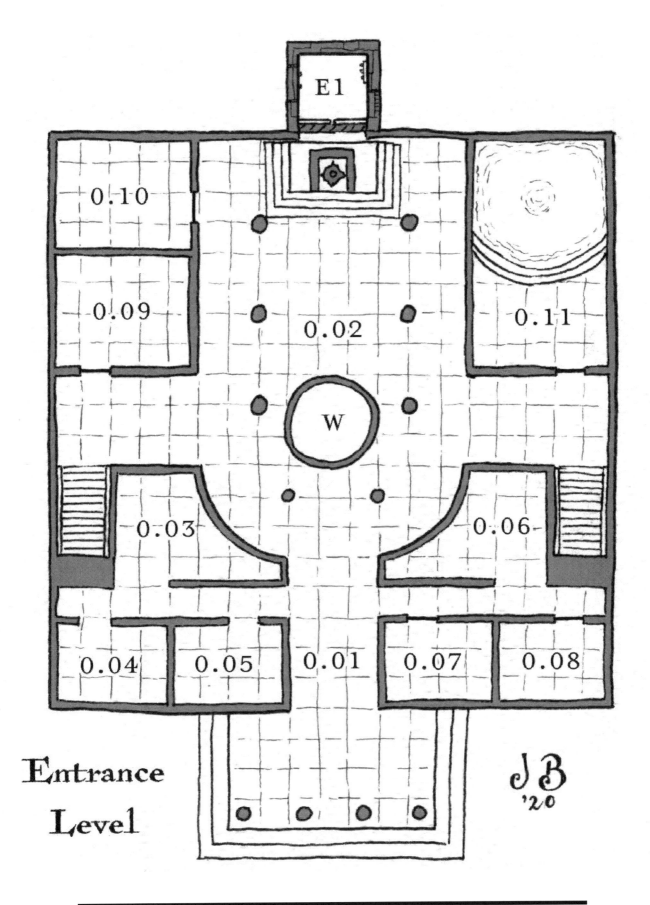

E1

0.10

0.09

0.02

0.11

W

0.03

0.06

0.04

0.05

0.01

0.07

0.08

Entrance
Level

JB '20

Pots. There are two ceramic pots in the room. Both pots are filled with dust, the decayed remains of potpourri.

Power Grid. A small channel has been carved into the floor. When the power grid is on, it glows blue. A creature that touches the blue light when the power grid is on takes 7 (2d6) lightning damage.

Well Shaft (W). The well shaft (see **area 1.02**) runs through the center of the temple. It cannot be entered via this level.

1.03 - The Weapons

When the power grid is on, this area reveals an altar covered in various weapons.

Altar. Noticing the presence of the altar before the power grid is turned on requires a DC 15 Wisdom (Perception) check. A character can use an action to pry the altar from the floor with a successful DC 22 Strength (Athletics) check. The front of the altar reads "Choose Wisely" in Draconic.

The altar has six weapons on top of it, each weapon held in place by leather loops pinned to the altar's surface. The leather loops open without too much trouble. Elves get a strange feeling when in the presence of the weapons, as if there is something otherworldly about each of them.

The weapons are:

• A longsword.
• A two-headed flail.
• A greataxe.
• A longbow.
• An ornate dagger.
• A mace.

The two-headed flail is a *hydra flail* (see Appendix C for details). An *identify* spell reveals the properties of the flail, but the other five items give no indication of their properties beyond being magical; this should be a hint that they are cursed.

A non-elven (full-blooded or half-elf) humanoid that touches one of the cursed weapons immediately ages 1d6

x 10 years. The aging effect can be reversed with a *remove curse* spell, but only within 24 hours of it occurring. The healing pool in **area 0.11** will also restore an aged humanoid even if its healing powers have been used up for the day.

1.04 - West Landing

The stairs lead back up to the western side of **area 0.02**. Part of the power grid is visible in the floor (see **areas 1.02** or **1.05** for details).

1.05 - Western Passage

This passage connects **areas 1.02**, **1.03**, **1.04**, **1.06**, and **1.10**.

Area Description. The area has the following features.

Pillars. Three large, 5-foot thick marble pillars hold the ceiling aloft.

Pots. There are four ceramic pots in the room. All of the pots are filled with dust, the decayed remains of potpourri. In the northeasternmost pot, on top of the dust, there is a key similar to the one Viothye carries around her neck. It operates the elevators the same as Viothye's.

Power Grid. A small channel has been carved into the floor. When the power grid is on, it glows blue. A creature that touches the blue light when the power grid is on takes 7 (2d6) lightning damage.

1.06 - Passageway

This passageway connects **area 1.05** to **1.07**.

Cubbies. There are eight cubbies in the western wall. They function the exact same as the cubbies detailed in **area 1.10**.

1.07 - Kathoraad's Tomb

This 20-foot-by-30-foot area hosts a large, unusually shaped sarcophagus in the center of the room.

Kathoraad's Tomb. The sarcophagus is magically sealed. The only way to open it is by destroying its "lid". The lid has AC 18, 50 hit points (damage threshold 5), and immunity to poison and psychic damage.

When the power grid is turned on, the lid melts away revealing a **stone golem** within—Kathoraad. Kathoraad regains 20 hit points at the start of its turn so long as it has 1 hit point remaining. If damage reduces Kathoraad to 0 hit points, it crumbles into rubble and it drops to 1 hit point instead. Kathoraad is then incapacitated and its movement is 0 until the end of its next turn. Only a *wish* spell cast on Kathoraad when it is reduced to rubble will stop it from reforming. Clever characters might separate Kathoraad's remains, slowing down its reformation process (GM's discretion).

Once revived, Kathoraad will patrol this level and destroy any creature it finds that does not possess one of the temple keys (see page 12). A creature with an temple key can use his or her action to issue basic commands to Kathoraad such as "stop", "attack", or "guard this corridor" with Kathoraad will do its best to follow. However, Kathoraad will not leave this level. If the switch in **area 1.12** is turn off, Kathoraad is disabled.

1.08 - Treasure Vault

This room stored the temple builders' coinage.

Treasure. In various sacks and small, wooden chests, the characters discover ancient currency unlike any they have likely ever seen. The currency is the equivalent of 322,700 cp.

1.09 - The Boulder

This smooth chamber is what is used to turn on the temple's power grid.

Area Description. This area has the following features:

Dimensions & Terrain. The walls of this area are unlike the rest in the temple. Instead of laid stone bricks, the walls appear to be lined with some sort of soft, bluish metal. The floor has a gentle slope starting at the boulder and ending at the south end of the westernmost corridor.

Floor Panel. A four-foot wide metal

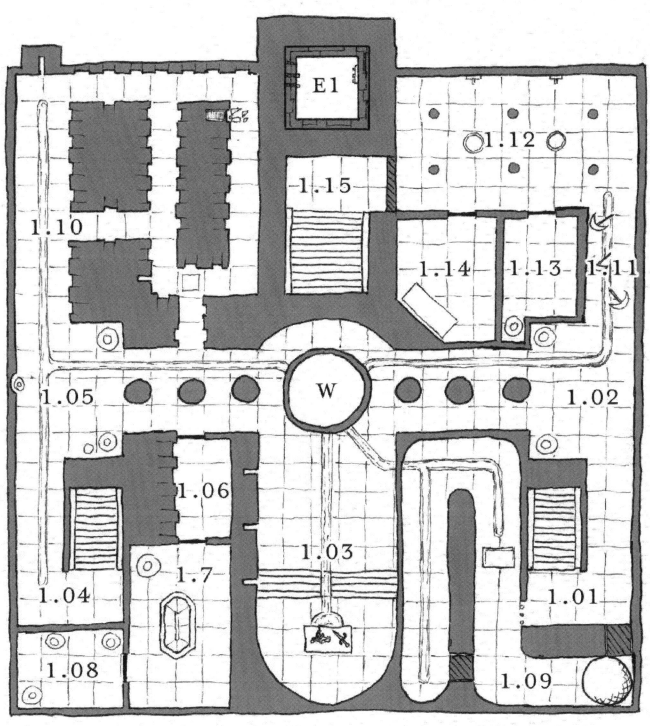

Level 1

JB
'20

panel rises out of the floor in the center of the easternmost hall. When 100 pounds of weight or more is placed on top of the panel, the two secret doors open and the boulder in the eastern corridor starts to roll along the path. Although the boulder will continue to roll, the secret doors only remain open as long as the panel remains pressed.

Power Grid. A small channel has been carved into the floor. When the power grid is on, it glows blue. A creature that touches the blue light when the power grid is on takes 7 (2d6) lightning damage.

Secret Doors. When the floor panel is pressed, it opens two secret doors. The first door is in the eastern side of the corridor, right next to the boulder. The second secret door connects the area's two corridors. Both doors are obvious, requiring only a successful DC 11 Wisdom (Perception) check to notice. A character can use his or her action to pry open a door with a successful DC 17 Strength (Athletics) check.

The Boulder. When the panel is pressed, the 5-foot diameter, 10 ton boulder at the east end of the area begins to roll through passage. The boulder rolls at a rate of 10 feet per round. As it rolls, arcane symbols glow all over its surface. As soon as the boulder touches the power grid channel, the power grid turns on. The boulder stops rolling once it reaches the southern end of the westernmost corridor.

If the boulder attempts to enter the same space as a creature, the creature must make a DC 15 Strength saving throw. On a successful saving throw, the creature keeps the boulder from rolling any further. However, the creature takes 7 (2d6) lightning damage from the boulder's symbols. The creature takes an additional 7 (2d6) lightning damage if it ends its turn and it is still holding the boulder back. If a creature fails its saving throw, the boulder runs the creature

over; the creature takes 7 (2d6) bludgeoning damage plus (2d6) lightning damage and is knocked prone in its space.

Outrunning the Boulder. The best way to deal with the boulder is to follow this protocol:

1. Press the panel to release the boulder.
2. Run through the passage that leads to **area 1.01** before the beam of light turn on.
3. Failing that, the character can rush to the far end of this area and escape through the secret door connecting the area's two corridors.

1.10 - The Archive

This area looks like an archive.

Area Description. This area has the following features:

Dimensions & Terrain. The archive consists of multiple corridors with small cubbies pocking the walls. The entire area radiates strong conjuration magic.

Hidden Panel. There is a hidden panel in the floor at the junction. Noticing the panel requires a successful DC 15 Wisdom (Perception) check. See "Cubbies" below for details on the panel's functions.

Power Grid. A small channel has been carved into the floor. When the power grid is on, it glows blue. A creature that touches the blue light when the power grid is on takes 7 (2d6) lightning damage.

Cubbies. Decorating the walls are dozens of 6-inch-by-6-inch cubbies. Including the cubbies in **area 1.04**, there are 86 cubbies in all. It is impossible to see into the cubbies—their contents are masked by magical darkness. *Dispel magic* temporarily removes the darkness in a single cubby for 1 minute. However, it also disables the interdimensional pockets within the cubby—once dispelled, there is only a 2-foot deep slot in the wall. Similarly, if 100 pounds is placed on the panel at the junction

(see the map on page 29) for at least 1 minute, nearly all of the cubbies are disabled as long as the weight remains. The only cubby that stays in place is the cubby that holds a small statue of a serpent.

Each time a creature places their hand into any of the cubbies other than the one that holds the serpent statue, roll a d20 and refer to the Cubby Random Effects table below to determine what happens to the creature.

Serpent Idol. One of the cubbies contains a small statue of a serpent that radiates faint transmutation magic. The cubby that holds the serpent idol is marked on the map on page 29. See **area 1.12** for details on its functionality.

Cubby Random Effects.

d20	Effect
1	The creature's arm is grappled by something (escape DC 13). While grappled, the creature is restrained and takes 2 (1d4) acid damage at the start of each of its turns.
2	Something bites the creature. The creature takes 2 (1d4) piercing damage.
3	The creature reaches into fire. The creature takes 3 (1d6) fire damage.
4	The creature reaches into a cold enviroment. The creature takes 3 (1d6) cold damage.
5-7	The creature pulls its arm back to discovered that it's covered in harmless, yellow slime.
8-10	The creature pulls its arm back to discover that it's covered in insects. The insects are harmless, but it's pretty icky.
11-20	Nothing happens.

1.11 - Path of Blades

When the power grid is off, the blades remain in place. Once the power is back on, these three dangerously sharp, enchanted blades can kill a creature with a single hit.

Blade Trap. A creature that enters this area for the first time or ends their turn in this hallway is attacked by the blades. The blades make three attacks with a +6 to hit. On a hit, a blade deals 12 (2d10 + 1) slashing damage. A creature hit by a blade must also make a DC 10 Strength saving throw. On a failed saving throw, the creature is knocked prone.

A character who investigates the ceiling from where the blades' shafts emerge will understand how the blades operate with a successful DC 13 Intelligence (Investigation) check. Once the character understands how they function, they can make a successful DC 15 Intelligence check using proficiency in thieves' tools to disable a single blade. Each magical blade has AC 19, 25 hp, resistance to bludgeoning, piercing, and flashing damage made by non-magical attacks and immunity to poison and psychic damage. A destroyed blade can no longer attack.

A character holding one of the temple keys is immune to the damage the blades do; the blades pass right through them almost as if the character wasn't there.

1.12 - Path of the Traveler

This unusual room will lead the characters further into the temple.

Area Description. This area has the following features:

Blast Door. A large, 10-foot-wide door leads to **area 1.15**. The door is made of the same soft metal that lines the walls in **area 1.09**. Like the elevator's "doors", the blast door connects directly with the floor, walls, and ceilings, so it can't be opened by brute force or through picking locks, and it is immune to all types of damage. The blast door can only

be opened by placing the two serpent idols in the braziers (see below).

Braziers. There are two braziers spaced 15-feet apart. When the power grid is off, the braziers remain unlit. When the power grids are lit, the braziers glow harmless blue flame. When the serpent idols from **area 1.10** and **1.14** are placed into the braziers (one each), the switches on the wall appear. In addition, the blast door opens.

Pillars. There are six, 1-foot-diameter pillars holding the ceiling aloft.

Secret Switches. There are two hidden switches in the northern wall. The switches only appear if both serpent idols are placed into the blue-flame braziers in the center of the room. The easternmost switch disables Kathoraad (see **area 1.07**) and the westernmost switch disables the blade trap (see **area 1.11**).

1.13 - Prayer Chamber

This old, dusty room has a decaying rug at the center of the floor. There is a ceramic pots in the southern alcove. The pot is filled with dust, the decayed remains of potpourri.

1.14 - Priest's Vestments

This ancient chamber was used to store the temple high priests' vestments.

Vestments. A table at the southwestern end of the room holds the temple priest's vestments. The table holds the following items:

- Cloth of gold vestments worth 25 gp.
- The *headdress of the serpent king* (see Appendix C for details). A small serpent idol. The idol is used to reveal the switches in **area 1.12**.

1.15 - Down

So long as the characters are able to open the blast door, they can enter this chamber. The reverse side of the blast door is covered in blood stains and there is feces all over the floor. The smell of urine is strong.

The stairs lead down to **area 2.01**.

Level 2 - Second Sub-Level

The moment the characters step off the stairs (or elevator) they notice that the place reeks of human filth.

Roots

Starting on the second sub-level and every level below it, strange, throbbing roots grow from the ceilings, walls, and floors. The roots are a side effect of the ship below the temple's core leaking into the soil surrounding the temple.

The clones on Level 2 gnaw on the roots for sustenance. In turn, their physiologies are affected by the raw transmutation energy in the roots making them highly unstable. A 5-foot area of root has AC 15, 50 hit points, and immunity to psychic damage. Unless the root takes fire or necrotic damage, it regains 1 hit point at the start of each hour so long as it has 1 hit point remaining. A creature that eats the root must make a DC 12 Constitution saving throw. On a failed saving throw, roll a d10 and refer to the Root Mutation table to determine what happens to the creature. All the mutations listed can be cured with a *greater restoration* spell or similar magic.

Root Mutation.

d10	Mutation
1-5	The creature starts to decay. The decaying creature can't regain hit points, and its hit point maximum decreases by 10 (3d6) for every 24 hours that elapse. If the decaying effect reduces the target's hit point maximum to 0, the target dies, and its body collapses into a pile of quivering, formless flesh.
6	Eyeballs start to form all over the creature's body. 1d4 eyeballs appear on the creature's flesh every 24 hours that pass. At first, it is a boon. The creature gains proficiency with the Perception skill and adds double its proficiency bonus to all Wisdom (Perception) checks that rely on sight. After 10 days, however, the growth spirals out of control. Each time the creature grows more eyeballs, it must make a DC 10 Constitution saving throw. On a failed saving throw, the creature's body destabilizes and it collapses into a pile of disembodied eyeballs.
7	The creature grows an extra arm. It takes 24 hours for the arm to grow large enough to be effective, and even then, it's weaker than the creature's other arms. The arm has a reach of 5 feet and it can lift a number of pounds equal to five times the creature's Strength score. The creature can use it to do the following simple tasks: lift, drop, hold, push, or pull an object or a creature, open or close a door or a container; grapple someone; or make an unarmed strike. The arm can't wield weapons or shields or do anything that requires manual precision, such as using tools or magic items or performing the somatic compents of a spell. There is a 50% chance that the arm has a mind of its own. An arm with a mind of its own functions like a sentient magic item. See Chapter 7 of the DMG for details.
8	The creature develops boney protrusions all over its body. The protrusions grant the creature the benefits of natural armor. When not wearing armor, the creature's AC is 13 + its Dexterity modifier (maximum of 2). The creature can use its natural armor to determine its AC if the armor it wears would leave it with a lower AC. Unfortunately, The protrusions cause intense pain. The creature makes all ability checks with disadvantage.
9	The creature's size doubles in all dimensions and its weight is multiplied by eight. This growth functions the same way as the enlarge feature of the *enlarge/reduce* spell, except it is permanent. Additionally, the creature's Intelligence score decreases by 4.
10	The creature's size is halved in all dimensions and its weight is reduced to one-eighth of normal. This reduction functions the same was as the reduce feature of the *enlarge/reduce* spell.

2.01 - Entry

This level goes even further away from the "ancient temple" look and more towards some sort of high-technology laboratory.

Area Description. The area has the following features:

Dimensions & Terrain. The stairs descend into a large chamber and split at the well tube that cuts through the center of the temple.

Hydra Statue. A statue of a multi-headed serpent stands before those who enter the area from the staircase. The statues are made of the curious soft metal found throughout the complex. Bits of root, daggers, and other offerings have been laid at its base.

Light. With the power grid on, blue-glowing arcane symbols on the wall illuminate the complex. Additionally, the torches on the wall glow with harmless, blue flame which casts dim light throughout.

Sounds. The hum of the power grid revererates through the complex. Grunts and sniffs made by the mishapen clones echo through the halls.

Creature Information. While the characters are exploring this room, something rushes past the hallway at the south end of this area (**area 2.02**) going east to west. Characters with successful DC 15 passive Wisdom (Perception) checks think that what they saw was a goblin of some sort.

2.02 - Hallway of Statues

This area has six statues built into alcoves in the northern wall.

Dulon Statues. Each statue has four triple-jointed arms and eight triple-jointed legs. Also, each statue has a different head. From west to east:

- The statue's neck is two feet long and ends in a star-shape. Each point of the star has what-looks-like an eyeball at the end.
- The statue has a wide, flat head with no eyes, nostrils, or ears—it only has a wide, toothy mouth.
- The statue splits into two heads, both which looks like the heads of a praying mantis.
- The statue's neck spirals and ends with a single fuzzy-ball at the end.
- The statue has no head. Instead, blue flame radiates from it like the torches.
- The statue lacks a head—instead, there is a copse of fronds that dangle from where its head would be.

All six statues are made of the same strange, soft metal found throughout the rest of the complex.

Creature Information. An **unstable clone** (see Appendix D) lingers in the shadows of this hallway. The moment the characters get close enough to get a better look at the creature, it

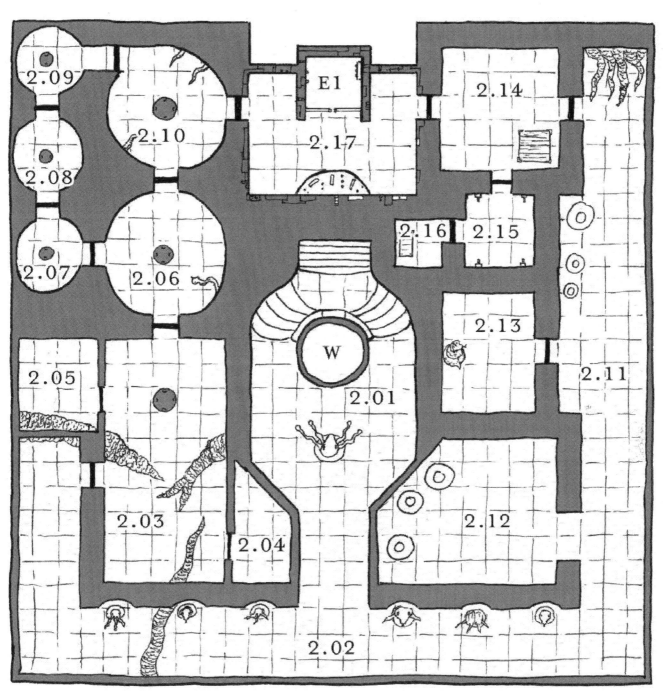

Level 2

JB
'20

turns, shrieks, and attacks. The creature's shrieks likely alert the other clones in the area.

2.03 - Clone Resting Chamber

An **overgrown clone** and five **unstable clones** use this area to rest. If the characters make any sounds while traveling through **areas 2.02** or **2.06**, the clones rush to find out the cause of the disturbance and attack. The entire room stinks of urine and feces.

2.04 - Empty Chamber

Other than clone dung smeared on the walls and floor, this chamber is empty.

2.05 - Dead Clone

A dead overgrown clone, victim of a fight with unstable clones, lies face down on the floor, rotting. It has bite marks on its body, clear signs of cannibalism.

2.06 - Small Cylindrical Room

Other than a column at the center of the room and piles of clone dung, there is nothing of interest here.

2.07 - Small Cylindrical Room

This cylindrical room has a stone column at its center.

Area Description. This room has the following features:

Column. A five-foot-diameter stone column is at the center of the room. The center of the column has been worn away by the unstable clones sharpening their daggers against its edges.

Daggers. There are six crude stone daggers on the floor.

Floor. The floor tiles have been pried up and shattered. The pieces are then used to create crude daggers for the unstable clones that inhabit this level.

Creature Information. Two **unstable clones** are here sharpening daggers. They attack the characters on sight.

Clones

There are two types of clones throughout this level. First, there are **unstable clones**. These clones look like short, dark-skinned goblins. Most are armed with crude daggers made of sharpened stone and torn canvas. Second are the **overgrown clones**. They look like large, dark-skinned ogres. The pain caused by their constantly changing bodies affects their psyche, driving them to rage.

Both types of clones are detailed further in Appendix D.

2.08 - Love Shack

Similar to **area 2.06**, there is a single column in this room holding the ceiling aloft. Two **overgrown clones** sleep in each other's arms at the center of this room. Like most of the clones on the level, they attack if disturbed.

2.10 - The Way is Barred

This cylindrical room has three doors leading to **areas 2.06**, **2.09**, and **2.17**.

Barred Door. The door leading to **area 2.17** is barred from the other side. Breaking the door open requires a successful DC 23 Strength (Athletics) check. It's clear that the clones have tried breaking the door open, but to no avail.

2.11 - Attack of the Clones

There are six **unstable clones** and one **overgrown clone** in this hallway. They attack the characters on sight.

Area Description. This area has the following features:

Dimensions & Terrain. Like many of the areas on this level, the floors are smeared with all manner of filth: blood, feces, sweat, and urine. In fact, it's so bad here, that a creature that takes the Dash action on their turn must first make a successful DC 12 Dexterity (Acrobatics) check or slip and fall prone in its space.

Barred Door. The door leading to **area 2.17** is barred from the other side. Breaking the door open requires a successful DC 23 Strength (Athletics) check. It's clear that the clones have tried breaking the door open, but to no avail.

Pots. There are three ceramic pots in the room. What's unusual is that none of them have been smashed by the clones. At the bottom of each of the pots is a strange, bluish liquid. A creature that drinks the liquid recovers from any diseases or conditions affecting it; the conditions can be blinded, deafened, paralyzed or poisoned. Sixty-six places the pots here to cure his "brothers" of any negative ailments caused by their condition. The liquid will not remove mutation effects created by consuming the roots.

2.12 - Stable Clones

This area is a little cleaner than the rest of the level.

Area Description. This area has the following features:

Dimensions & Terrain. This area is 25-feet wide north-to-south and 20-feet wide east-to-west. The ceilings are marginally shorter than those found throughout the rest of the level.

Pots. There are three ceramic pots in this room. Like the pots in **area 2.11**, they were placed here by Sixty-six. The largest pot contains food rations. The other two pots have the same magical liquid described in **area 2.11**.

Creature Description. Three, bald-headed, dark-skinned clones are huddled in the room. The three men (whose names are Sixty, Seventy-four, and Eighty-five) are all **commoners** armed with daggers. They don't speak, but they are also non-violent. Unlike their rambunctious brethren, they have tried to maintain their intelligence. However, isolation has still made them skeptical of any intruders that enter the area. If a character is able to persuade them that they mean them no harm, they can only give enough directions to lead the characters to **area 2.14**.

2.13 - Hydra Room

The door that leads into this room is hanging off its hinges. A statue of a hydra similar to the one in **area 2.01** stands against the western wall. Bits of root, daggers, and other offerings have been laid at its base as well. There is nothing else of interest here.

2.14 - Passage

This area connects **areas 2.11**, **2.15**, and **2.17**.

Area Description. This area has the following features.

Dimensions & Terrain. This area is a 25-foot-square with 10-foot high ceilings. Notably, the area is devoid of the same filth found throughout the rest of the level.

Barred Door. Unless the characters came in through the door from **area 2.12**, the door leading to **area 2.12** has been barred from inside this room. The bars are made of solid wood held into place by crude hinges attached to the wall. The bars are further reinforced by steel rods wedged between the bars and a hole cut into the tiles in the floor. All of this is easy to remove from this side.

Crate. There is a large, wooden crate at the center of the room. The crate looks much newer than the rest of the temple, and looks like it probably came from outside. Although the crate is empty, a successful DC 12

Intelligence (Investigation) check reveals that there was once fresh fruit, bread, and preserved meats within—rations. Sixty-six removed the rations and took them back to his lair on the third level.

2.15 - Grid Control

This area controls various elements of the temple.

Area Description. This area has the following features:

Door. The door leading to **area 2.16** is similar to the elevator doors and the blast door in **areas 1.12/1.15**. The door connects directly with the floor, walls, and ceilings, so it can't be opened by brute force or through picking locks, and it is immune to all types of damage. Only a creature with one of the temple keys (see page 12) can open the door. The door remains open as long as a creature stands near it. Otherwise, it closes after one round.

Switches. There are two switches on the north wall and two switches on the south wall. Switching all the switches into the up position returns the boulder in **area 1.09** to its starting position and turns off the grid. Inversely, switching them all to the down position sends the boulder into its final position and turns on the grid.

2.16 - Azure Odonburgite Core

The *azure odonburgite* (see Appendix C) core that powers the entire complex is kept in this area.

Area Description. This area has the following features:

Dimensions & Terrain. This room is a 10-foot wide square with 5-foot high ceilings.

Steel-Lined Walls. The walls are lined with soft steel.

Odonburgite Core. A stone box with a heavy stone lid rests against the western wall. One or more creatures with combined Strength scores of 15 or higher can remove the lid. Once they do, intense blue light shines out of the box. When this occurs, each creature within 20 feet of the box must succeed on a DC 15 Constitution saving throw. A creature takes 10 (3d6) radiant damage and is poisoned on a failed saving throw, or takes half as much damage and isn't poisoned on a successful one. Each creature that ends its turn within 20 feet of the core must repeat its saving throw with similar consequences. Placing the core into a heavy stone or lead-lined box will protect creatures from its radiation. However, if the core is placed into an extradimensional space such as a *bag of holding* or *portable hole*, the extradimensional space implodes, sending the contents of the extradimensional space into the Astral Plane.

The core itself is a bright blue gem wired into place—*azure odonburgite*. If the gem is removed, the power grid ceases to function.

The gem is worth 5,000 gp to anyone that can understand its function.

2.17 - Control Room

Any illusion of this being an "ordinary temple" should end the moment the characters set foot in this area.

Area Description. This area has the following features:

Dimensions & Terrain. The walls here are made of the same strange steel found throughout the temple. When the power is on, there are blue-glowing symbols built into the wall.

Barred Door. Unless the characters

came in through the door from **area 2.10**, the door leading to that area has been barred from inside this room. The bars are made of solid wood held into place by crude hinges attached to the walls. The bars are further reinforced by steel rods wedged between the bars and a hole cut into the tiles in the floor. All of this is easy to remove from this side.

Elevator E1. A pair of doors similar to those found in **area 0.02** block the entrance to the elevator. A creature holding one of the temple keys (see page 12) can will the doors open by waving they key in front of it. A detailed description of this elevator can be found in **area 0.02.**

Sounds. The entire room emits a low hum.

Control Console. The most striking feature of this area is the massive control console against the southern wall. A creature who spends one hour observing the console and makes a successful DC 15 Intelligence (Arcana) check can understand its functions and everything it can do.

Here are all of the things that the console controls:

- Opens or closes all magically sealed doors throughout the complex (including the elevator doors and the blast door in **area 1.12**).
- Lowers or raises the elevators.
- Shuts off the necrotic exhaust coming through the well shaft.
- Commands and remote controls Kathoraad.
- Lowers or raises the weapon altar in **area 1.03**.
- Reveals or masks the cubbies in **areas 1.04** and 1.10.
- Disables or enables the blade trap in **area 1.11**.
- Refreshes the embalming fluids in the clone vats throughout Level 3.
- The self-destruct sequence can be armed via the panel, but only by a creature that knows the sufficient password (such as Sixty-six.)

Level 3 - The Laboratory

The "temple" is obviously no temple now, but instead, a disguise for the technological nightmare that is its lower levels. This entire facility was once an entire laboratory dedicated to recreation of humanoid clones.

General Features

Unless stated otherwise, Level 3 has the following features.

Dimensions & Terrain. The floors, walls, and ceiling are made from curiously soft steel. The ceilings are high here, 30-feet in most areas.

Cloning Vats. At regular intervals throughout this level are tall, cylindrical sarcophagi made of thick, semi-opaque glass sitting on steel bases. Each vat contains a dead clone who has been preserved by the chamber's fluids. The clones are in varying stages of maturity; some are embryonic, others look like fully-grown adults. There are even a few with mutations: multiple eyes, tentacles for feet, extra arms, etc.

Doors. All of the doors on this level are made of the same soft metal as the floors, walls, and ceilings. However, they are completely attached to the frames in which they stand. Only a creature holding one of the temple keys can open the doors by waving the key in front of it. The doors can be destroyed—they have AC 21, 100 hit points (damage threshold 10), and immunity to poison and psychic damage as well as damage from bludgeoning, piercing, and slashing made with nonmagical attacks.

Lights. Unless the power grid is off, panels placed at regular intervals emit bright blue light for 20 feet and dim blue light for an additional 20 feet.

Roots. Gargantuan, mutated roots push through the walls, floors, and ceilings of this area. See page 31 for details.

Sounds & Smells. The entire level emits a low hum as long as the power grid is running. Otherwise, it is mostly quiet. Everything smells a little like burning leather throughout the level.

3.01 - Entry Chamber

Likely, the characters enter this level via Elevator E1. This is where they first meet Sixty-six (see below).

Area Description. This area has the following features:

Dimensions & Terrain. This area looks similar to the other areas on this level except its ceilings are 50-feet high. The blue light doesn't extend to the ceiling, giving the place the illusion that its ceiling is endless. The well shaft cuts through the center of the room.

Control Console. At the southeastern end of the room is another control console. The control console functions the same as the one described in **area 2.17.**

Pillars. There are eight cylindrical pillars spread evenly around the well shaft. Each pillar is only 15-feet high.

Creature Information. The clone named Sixty-six is found here hunched over the control console. Sixty-six does not seem surprised by the characters' appearance. Sixty-six uses the **cloned sorcerer** stat block (see Appendix D), except he is armed with an antimatter rifle (as described in Chapter 9 of the *DMG*) with only 1 shot remaining. He is protected by a **shield guardian** named Gar. Sixty-six's alignment is neutral.

Sixty-six looks like a 70-year-old human male with kinky, gray hair, a wild, unkempt beard, and dark skin. He is wearing old, tattered blue and red robes. A character who succeeds on a DC 15 Intelligence (History) check recognizes the robes as being of Dinzer design, but centuries old.

His arm is wounded—he was clawed by Barbakis, but Sixty-six managed to hit Barbakis with a shot from his anti-matter rifle, scaring off the fiend.

What Does He Want? Sixty-six has lived in the belly of the temple most

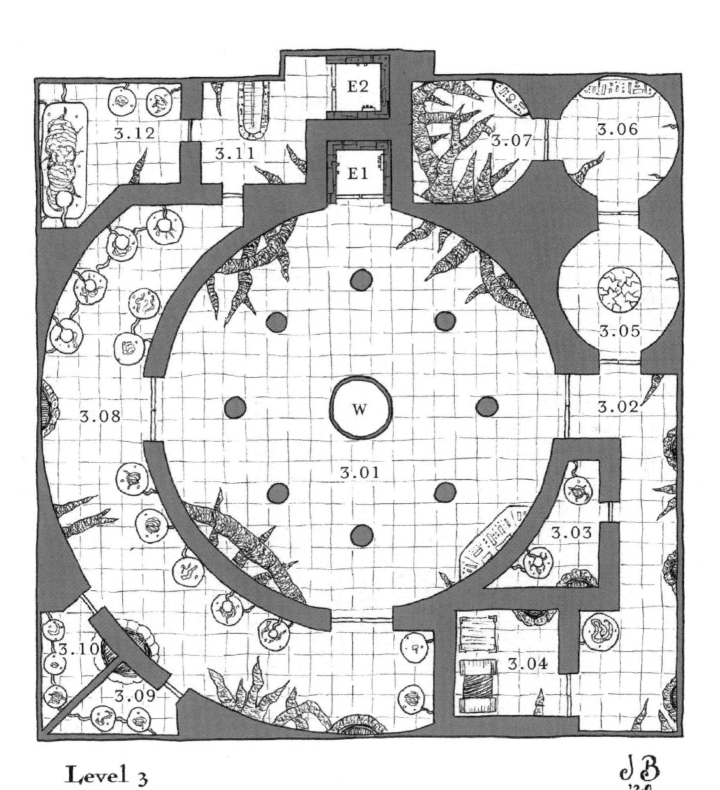

Level 3

of his long life. He has no interest in escaping, but he is interested in protecting its secrets from the rest of the world. Just as the characters were discovering the old clone, Sixty-six was finishing the protocol to establish a self-destruct sequence. On the view screen just above the control console (and every other screen throughout the temple) strange characters rotate and diminish—a character who succeeds on a DC 10 Intelligence check realizes that it's a countdown of sorts.

What Does He Know? Although there isn't much time, Sixty-six will share what he knows without provocation:

"Nearly 1,500 years ago, this temple was founded by six powerful beings called dulons. The dulons created the humans and the elves. And they also created two more races before those races. First, they created the titans, twelve legendary creatures whose powers know no bounds. Most of the titans are gone or resting now, but one such titan—Grihoo the Traveler—lives below this temple. From Grihoo's blood, the dulons then created the second race, the danaavrakti. Immediately, the dulons realized they'd made a mistake creating the danaavrakti; they were cruel fiends, focused only on their own goals. The danaavrakti wanted to erase the creatures spawned by the titans and dulons from Casar and recreate the Cosmos in their own image. Like the titans, the danaavrakti were limited to twelve and they could not propagate their species."

The old man coughs into his hand. Blood. He's dying.

"Eventually, one of the dulons—the greatest of their kind, a dulon named Maf—took his Cosmoship to this location and built this temple over Grihoo. Maf believed that if he could combine the best elements of the four progenitor races—titans, danaavrakti, humans, and elves—

he could create a creature capable of reversing the forces that tear at the fabric of reality.

"After a millennia of study and experimentation, he created two such creatures who were nearly perfect: myself and my brother. We both left to the mainland and started new lives. But I've always felt the call of this location and the titan below it. So after some time, I returned.

"For the next few centuries, Maf and I worked to create more and more of my brethren. Most lacked magical abilities, but they possessed the same long-livedness that I did. Many of those failed experiments are now on the second level of this temple. But there were some who were nearly complete successes."

The old man pauses and stares at the floor; it's clear his mind is elsewhere. After a moment, he turns back to you and smiles.

"Maf and I also built the pylons across the land to hide this temple as well as other clues that would lead those back here. Not too long ago, something destroyed the tower that control the pylons, revealing us to the world. And now there is a danaavrakt in this temple. The creature injured me and fled to the basement. It believes that if it can claim a portion of Grihoo's power, it can amplify its power and potentially finish what others of its kind started: the destruction of the world.

"If you can't stop the danaavrakt, I have no choice but to destroy this temple and the island. You have ten minutes."

Sixty-six has *mindblanked* himself. Nothing the character can do will force him to turn off the self-destruct sequence.

3.02 - Eastern Corridor
This long corridor connects **areas 3.01**, **3.03**, **3.04**, and **3.05**.

10 Minutes Until The End

The characters have 1d4 + 10 minutes to find Barbakis and defeat him. Don't let the characters know exactly how much time there is. Barbakis is in **area 4.05**. If the characters don't already have an temple key, Sixty-six gives the characters' his and gives them directions to Elevator E2.

Set a timer to 10 minutes in real time. The players must navigate their characters down the elevator rush to **area 4.05** and fight Barbakis. Because certain in-game actions take more or less time in real life, be sure to stop the timer and add or subtract time to it when necessary. For example, a single round of combat only takes 6 seconds of game-time, but can run for 10 minutes or more in real time.

If the characters fail to reach and stop Barbakis in time, the portal generator in **area 3.05** destabilizes and collapses. Within 6 seconds, everything within a 6 mile radius sphere of the temple is temple vanishes in a bright flash.

3.03 - Child Clones
The clones in the clone vats in this area matured to the age of young children before perishing.

3.04 - Fluid Reprocessor
All of the clone vats' liquids flow back to the machine at the western wall which magically purifies the liquids and reuses it throughout the complex. If the machine is turned off or destroyed, the clones will start to decay in a week.

3.05 - Portal Generator
The moment the characters enter this area, they are bathed in intense black light. At the center of the room is a massive, spherical hunk of *kalapatr* (see Appendix C for details). Nodes and wires are attached to it at all sides. If a creature touches the *kalapatr*, they take 7 (2d6) necrotic

damage and they must make a DC 13 Charisma saving throw. On a failed saving throw, the creature is transported to a random plane of existence somewhere in the Cosmos (GM's discretion) for 1 minute, as if banished by the *banishment* spell. The creature returns to the exact same spot that it left.

3.06 - Portal Controls

The control console in this area functions the same as the control consoles throughout the rest of the temple, except it also activates the portal generator. A character who spends 1 hour studying the console can make a DC 15 Intelligence (Arcana) check to discover the following:

The console can transport the entirety of the Temple of Grihoo into another plane of existence. A character who understands how to use the portal controls (see **area 3.06** for details) can choose any of the planes of existence listed below. However, a character who does not understand how the controls work may accidentally shunt the temple to a random plane of existence. Furthermore, if the temple self-destructs, roll randomly to determine to which plane of existence the temple and the island are transported.

d20	Plane of Existence
1	The Burn
2	The Construct
3	The Chaos
4	The Cruel
5	The Crumble
6	The Dark
7	The Depth
8	The Dream
9	The Inevitable
10	The Other
11	The Void
12-20	Random pocket dimension

3.07 - Overgrown Room

This room is overgrown with the mutated roots. The control console in the northeastern corner no longer functions.

3.08 - Main Corridor

There are 13 clone vats in this long, curved hallway, each in varying stages of maturity/mutation.

3.09 - Embryonic Clones

The clones in the vats in this area are in very early stages of development.

3.10 - Early Rejections

Similar to **area 3.10**, the clones in the vats here are in very early stages of development. They are also extremely mutated, hardly recognizable as human embryos.

3.11 - Root Experiments

At the northern end of this area, the top half of a mutated root has been sliced open and peeled back. Already, it's starting to regenerate with small polyps forming on its exposed flesh.

The polyps inhale and exhale like humanoid lungs.

Elevator E2. The temple's second elevator—which connects Levels 3

and 4—is here. Just like the first elevator, the elevator is protected by a featureless door. Only an elevator key will "melt" the door away, revealing the elevator behind it.

Time Considerations. If the characters are doing good with time, have them wait 20-30 seconds (in real-time) while the elevator lowers down into the temple. Make sure to make a very loud "hmmmmm" sound to further torture them while they watch the seconds on the clock drain away.

3.12 - Maf's Tomb

There are two full grown clones in the vats in this area.

Maf's Cocoon. On top of a dais at the western end of this room, there is what-appears-to-be a cocoon made of hard, pink, ridged glass. Although the shell is mostly opaque, if the characters succeed on a DC 12 Wisdom (Perception) check they can make out the form of a strange, aberrant creature. The creature has four triple-jointed arms and eight triple-jointed legs. Instead of a head, the creature has a flat slap—almost like a hairbrush with no bristles—from which eight curved teeth-like protrusions stick out.

When Maf died, his body crystalized. Sixty-six laid him to rest in this area. If the glass shell is broken, Maf's body crumbles to dust.

Level 4 - The Cosmoship

Centuries ago, the dulon Maf landed his ship in the jungles above Grihoo's lair. Grihoo, recognizing its creator, felt at ease with Maf's return. Later, Maf and Sixty-six constructed the Dinzer pylons to mask the island from the mainland.

General Features

Unless stated otherwise, the Cosmoship has the following features.

Dimensions & Terrain. There are hardly any hard angles to be found throughout the ship. The walls, ceilings, and floors of the ship blend seamlessly into one another. The ceilings ascend to 10-feet throughout. The entire vehicle is made of the same soft metal found on the levels above it.

Doors. All of the doors on this level are made of the same soft metal as the floors, walls, and ceilings. However, they are completely attached to the frames in which they stand. Only a creature holding one of the elevator keys can open the doors by waving the key in front of it. The doors can be destroyed—they have AC 21, 100 hit points (damage threshold 10), and immunity to poison and psychic damage as well as damage from bludgeoning, piercing, and slashing made with nonmagical attacks.

False Clone Vats. The roots that grow through this level have flowered their own mockery of the clone vats from the level above. The vats look like flower bulbs with translucent film instead of glass. The creatures inside the vats look similar to the rest of the clones, but have a greenish tint to their skin as if they were plant life-forms. None of them are still alive.

Lights. Strips of light and multiple

Kalapatr

The four engines of this level have large, spherical *kalapatr* stones at their centers. Nodes and wires are attached to the spheres at all sides. If a creature touches the *kalapatr*, they take 7 (2d6) necrotic damage and they must make a DC 13 Charisma saving throw. On a failed saving throw, the creature is transported to a random plane of existence somewhere in the Cosmos (GM's discretion) for 1 minute, as if banished by the *banishment* spell. The creature returns to the exact same spot that it left.

---

panels radiate dim blue light.

Roots. Gargantuan, mutated roots push through the walls, floors, and ceilings of this area. See page 31 for details.

Rubble. Years ago, an arcane battle occurred on this level. Part of the ship was damaged in the fray, resulting in rubble strewn throughout the complex.

Sounds & Smells. The smell of burned leather is much stronger here, especially near the large, boiling pool at the center of the ship. The humming sound here is just as loud as it was in the laboratory.

4.01 - Engine Room

This massive, spherical room is one of the ship's four gate-engines. It is powered by *kalapatr*.

4.02 - Passage

Before the ship was damaged, this area opened into **area 4.04**. It is now cordoned off by a huge pile of rubble that blocks passage to the west. It will take the characters twenty minutes to clear away enough rubble to create an opening large enough to crawl through to **area 4.04**.

4.03 - Engine Room

This massive, spherical room is one of the ship's four gate-engines. It is powered by *kalapatr*.

Control Console. There is control console similar to the one found in **area 2.17**, 3.01, and 3.06 here. It still fucntions.

4.04 - Exhaust Chamber

The four engines are connected to this huge chamber.

Area Description. This area has the following features:

Dimensions & Terrain. The ceilings are marginally higher here, reaching 15-feet in height.

Control Console. A large control consoles dominates the southern end of the room. It functions exactly like the console in **area 3.06** (see page 39).

Footprints. A successful DC 15 Wisdom (Perception) check depicts the presence of footprints. The footprints give hints that a creature—humanoid—stumbled from **area 4.05** to **area 4.06**. The creature then left **area 4.06** and returned to the center of this area, just before the vat of mautka paanee. The footprints stopped there, seemingly disappearing into the well-shaft in the ceiling.

Levitation Panel. Just below where Elevator E1 would land, there is a soft, metallic bulge in the floor. This is the levitation panel that repels or attracts the elevator. (A similar one exists just below the floor of Elevator E2.)

Well Shaft (W). The well shaft that runs through the center of the temple terminates here in the ceiling just above the vat of mautka paanee. Because the vat extends five feet in all directions from the opening, a creature that descends into this layer from the shaft will need to succeed on a DC 15 Dexterity (Acrobatics) check to avoid falling in the caustic fluid.

Mautka Paanee. At the center of this area is a 25-foot-wide, 5-foot deep pool of mautka paanee. The first time a creature steps into the pool, it must make a DC 20 Constitution saving throw. On a failed saving throw, the creature is instantly destroyed in a

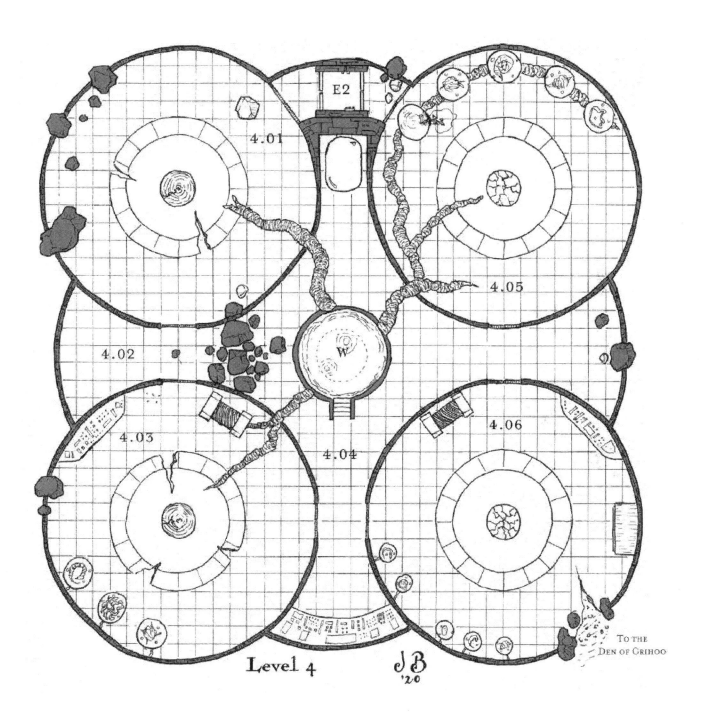

E2

4.01

4.05

4.02

W

4.03

4.04

4.06

Level 4

JB
'20

To the
Den of Grihoo

flash of light. On a successful saving throw, the creature takes 36 (8d8) radiant damage and is paralyzed. A creature that starts its turn in the vat is instantly destroyed. Nonmagical objects made of any material other than the steel from which the ship was built are also instantly destroyed.

4.05 - Engine Room

This massive, spherical room is one of the ship's four gate-engines. It is powered by *kalapatr*.

An Escapee?. Interestingly, the easternmost vat has been broken open. A successful DC 12 Intelligence (Investigation) check reveals that whatever was in there escaped recently. Footprints lead away from the broken vat to the door.

4.06 - Engine Room

This massive, spherical room is one of the ship's four gate-engines. It is powered by *kalapatr*.

Area Description. This area has the following features:

Control Console. There is control console similar to the ones found in **area 2.17**, **3.01**, and **3.06** here. It still functions.

Footprints. The footprints from **area 4.04** lead enter this area, cross the room, stop at the wardrobe, then turn around back to the door. It's clear that whoever it was that escaped from **area 4.05** grabbed something out of the wardrobe then returned to **area 4.04**.

Hole. A hole has been blasted into the southeastern corner of this area. The hole leads to Grihoo's Den (see Part 8). Standing near the hole, the characters can hear Barbakis shouting "I am your child, your servant! I am your true heir!" in Infernal.

Wardrobe. Extremely out of place on a space ship, there is a wooden wardrobe resting against the eastern wall of this area. Inside the wardrobes are brightly colored with strange, high-collars. One of the outfits is missing.

Part 8. Grihoo the Traveler

When the characters leave through the hole in the wall in **area 4.06**, they find themselves in a labyrinth of crudely-dug tunnels. The tunnels go left, right, up, and down—almost randomly. The sounds of Barbakis shouting, commanding Grihoo can be heard all throughout.

Navigating Grihoo's Labyrinth

When the characters enter Grihoo's labyrinth, they must find their way to Grihoo. The easiest way to do this is to follow the sound of Barbakis' voice. Have the players roll initiative, and roll initiative for Barbakis (a **rakshasa**) and Grihoo as well (Grihoo gets a +2 bonus to initiative checks). Each round, one character can use his or her action to make a Wisdom (Perception) check. Refer to the Navigating the Labyrinth table below to determine the result of the check.

Once you know the result of the check, roll on the Tunnel Direction table to determine the type of tunnel that the characters must travel through. Unless the result of the Navigating the Labyrinth roll was 20 or higher, the characters must continue to make Wisdom checks and find their way through the tunnels.

Time Considerations. When the characters enter initiative order, you can stop the timer.

Grihoo's Den

Once the characters get free of the labyrinth, they enter Grihoo's massive den.

Area Description

Grihoo's Den has the following features:

Dimensions & Terrain. Grihoo's den is huge. The chamber is a 100-foot wide circle with 100-foot high ceilings.

Light. There is no light in the den and the labyrinth. Both Grihoo and Barbakis have darkvision.

Pillars. Six colossal stone pillars rise up and attached to beams of

Navigating the Labyrinth.

Result	Outcome
9 or less	The characters get lost in the tunnels. Their next check to navigate the labyrinth is made with disadvantage.
10-14	The characters continue through the labyrinth.
15-19	The characters get closer to finding their way out of the labyrinth. Their next check to navigate the labyrinthe is made with advantage.
20+	The characters find a passage that leads direclty to Grihoo's Den.

Tunnel Direction.

d6	Direction
1	The characters must travel left.
2	The characters must travel right.
3	The characters must travel up. Climbing up requires a successful Strength (Athletics) check with a DC of 2d6 + 5.
4	The characters must travel down. Climbing down without sliding down the passage requires a successful Strength (Athletics) check with a DC of 2d6 + 5.
5-7	The characters must continue forward.
8	1d4 **Heads of Grihoo** (see Appendix D) attack the characters from one or more tunnels. The characters cannot go the way they were supposed to and must find another way.

hewn stone. Beyond the columns and the ceilings above the walls are pocked with multiple tunnels big enough for Grihoo's many heads to escape.

Grihoo

The most striking feature of Grihoo's Den is the titan itself. Grihoo is a superhydra, the progenitor of all serpents and reptiles on Casar. Grihoo has no body. Instead, the titan is nothing more than a mess of tangled serpents that seemingly have no beginning or end. Grihoo's heads can magically extend themselves as far as Grihoo needs them to, up to hundreds of feet if necessary. See Appendix D for details on the **heads of Grihoo**.

Creature Information

Barbakis, in his true danaavrakt form, stands before Grihoo. His face looks like a tiger's, but the stripes of his fur writhe like a nest of snakes. Glowing red mist seeps out of his mouth when he speaks. Functionally, Barbakis is a **rakshasa**.

What Does He Want? Barbakis wants to steal Grihoo's might and conjuration abilities. Already, he has absorbed some of the titan's energies. Fortunately, the wound he suffered at the hands of Sixty-six's anti-matter rifle has slowed him down considerably (he only has 80 hit points remaining). Unless he feels threatened, he will mostly ignore the characters and instead focus on absorbing Grihoo's might. At the start of each of

Barbakis' turns, he can use his action to make a DC 20 Charisma check. On a successful check, he gains a portion of Grihoo's power. If Barbakis succeeds on five checks, he completely steals Grihoo's power. At that point, Barbakis cannot be defeated. Only the destruction of the temple and the resulting shunt of the temple into another plane of existence will spare Casar from Barbakis' wrath—temporarily.

Lair Actions. Distracted by his goal to absorb Grihoo's power, Barbakis instead uses lair actions to defend himself. On initiative count 20 (losing initiative ties), Barbakis takes a lair action to cause one of the following effects.

- Barbakis commands up to six of **heads of Grihoo** to attack the characters.
- Barbakis uses one of his innate at-will or 3/day spells.

Freeing Grihoo. A character wielding the *hydra-flail* feels an odd surge each time they witness Barbakis attempt to steal Grihoo's power. When Barbakis makes a Charisma check to steal Grihoo's power, the character can make a contested Charisma check. An elf character wielding the flail makes this check with advantage. If the character's Charisma check is higher than Barbakis', Barbakis attempt to steal a portion

of Grihoo's power fails. Additionally, Barbakis cannot command Grihoo's heads on the next initiative count 20.

Barbakis then turns his attention to the character and the flail.

Variant Endings. If the characters are too tired/weak or too rested/strong going into this final combat, there are two variants included in the Addendum overleaf.

Concluding the Adventure: The Cataclysm

Even if the characters stop Barbakis, they learn a horrifying truth: Sixty-six lied. He never intended to stop the self-destruct sequence. The portal generator in **area 3.05** destabilizes and the entirety of the temple and the island is thrust into a random plane of existence.

If the characters saved Grihoo from Barbakis, the superhydra collects all of its heads before its saviors. Its many eyes stare at the characters briefly before they all start to glow with black energy. Then, the flash of light from the explosion washes over them and Grihoo disappears.

When the light fades, the characters find themselves in a distant saltwater wetlands. In the distance, they see a city—Naqqad. They're back in Omeria.

However, Grihoo, Barbakis, the island, and the temple are gone.

Addendum: Man & Boy Optional Subplot

For twenty-five years, Man has lived on The Skeleton Key as a prisoner of the Serpent Whisperers. The warrior women used him as a zukterin, or breeder, to help propagate their race. He remembers very little before then, but he does remember the tunnels below the temple and the monsters that live there. The only other clue to his history was the large scar on the back of his neck.

One day an explosion erupted from the temple. When the dust settled, a boy emerged, his eyes aglow. Flames shot from the boy's hands and his flesh swirled like water. The Serpent Whisperers, fearful of the supernatural, backed away. The boy then fled into the forest, and Man, seeing his opportunity to escape, followed him. The two have protected each other since.

Hundreds of miles from civilization with no formal knowledge of the world beyond the small island, they have very few options. Like Man, Boy has marks on the back of his neck; but instead of a large scar, Boy's markings are symbols in a language Man does not recognize.

How to Use This Resource

This sub-plot contains events and actions of the NPCs Man and Boy that coincide with the main plot presented in the *Grihoo* adventure module. Although it's possible that the characters discover Man and Boy earlier in the adventure, many of the events involve the presence of Qiu Xiang, the dragonborn knight who is a part of Theo Barbakis' crew.

Each section of this resource identifies the actions Man, Boy, and Qiu Xiang take during select chapters of *Grihoo*. Some of the actions are taken "off-screen", and work as background information for you, the GM.

Part 1. Life Among the Serpent Whisperers

As the characters work to earn the trust of the Serpent Whisperers, Viothye, the Serpent Whisperers' leader, approaches the characters with a task. She wants them to track a pair of men who escaped the temple and fled into the forest. She will not explain why the men were in the temple or why they are important but promises that if the characters can find them—alive or dead—they will earn the trust of herself and the other Serpent Whisperers.

Abandoned Mine

Man and Boy can be found in the abandoned mine on the western edge of the nameless mountain range.

Area Information. This area has the following general features.

Dimensions & Terrain. When the characters find the mine, read:

> Pushing past trees, you come upon what looks like an old mining fort in the side of a cliff, probably a few decades old, consumed by the aggressive flora of the jungle. The crude, timber portcullis that once blocked entry into the mine rests against the stone pillars at either side of it. You doubt that it's still operational, but it looks like one can squeeze between the timbers were one so inclined.

Lighting. If the characters approach in the day time, the entrance to the mine itself is well lit by the sun above.

Creature Information. Hiding inside the mine are **Man** and **Boy** (see Appendix D). Unless the characters were particularly stealthy as they approached the mine, Man is waiting inside the mine, standing just a few feet to the north of the entrance into the mine. Meanwhile, Boy is hiding closer to the northern tower.

Objectives and Goals. Man and

Boy are on the run from the Serpent Whisperers of Grihoo. Once Man recognizes that the characters are not the Serpent Whisperers, he will attempt to make a truce with the characters. Read the following:

> The man backs away and lowers his weapon. You get a good look at him. His clothing is a hodgepodge of random armor, leather, and animal furs. The exposed parts of his flesh reveal dark, scarred skin. He hides his face behind the cowl of a bronze helmet. His beard is dark and kinky, touching his chest.
>
> "I do not wish to fight. Boy and I only wish to escape the Serpent Whisperers."
>
> A boy steps out from the darkness behind the man. No older than 10, the boy is thin, exhausted-looking, and wearing only a tan loincloth. He has dark eyes, dark skin, and a mess of kinky, black hair on top of his head. If you didn't know any better, you'd guess he was a Dinzer.

Man and Boy want nothing more than to be left alone. Man won't risk the life of Boy but will try to escape with Boy into the forest (or even the mine if he has to). If the characters leave them alone, they promise that they will do anything they can to repay them.

What Do They Know? Man and Boy have suffered greatly at the hands of the Serpent Whisperers and the creatures who live in the Temple. They know that the Serpent Whisperers have a poor view towards most men in general and neither wishes to return. Although they don't entirely understand the powers that Boy possesses, they know it has something to do with what's happening in the Temple.

Treasure. Among the building supplies found in the abandoned mine, the characters can discover *gloves of amphibios* (see Appendix C).

Part 3. Arrival

Shortly after Theo Barbakis and his crew arrive, Barbakis and Qiu Xiang learn from Dexece that a man and a young boy escaped the temple. The pair start covertly interviewing everyone in the Serpent Whisperers' village, including the characters.

Inevitably, Barbakis tasks Qiu Xiang (dragonborn **knight**) with finding Man and Boy. The characters see the dragonborn knight pack a week's worth of rations and head north. Whether or not the characters follow him is up to them. If they question Qiu Xiang, he may offer that the characters accompany him to find the pair.

Back to the Mine

Eventually, Qiu Xiang discovers the same abandoned mine mentioned above. He treats with Man and Boy and shows empathy with their situation. He explains that he can help Man and Boy leave the island via *Three Hands Down* and offers to escort them back to the ship. While Boy seems reluctant, Man is anxious to leave the island.

Part 4. Sabotage!

When the characters, Qiu Xiang, Man, and Boy arrive at *Three Hands Down*, they discover Theo Barbakis distraught. The events of Part 4 transpire the same way they do in the *Grihoo* adventure, except Qiu Xiang explains that he hopes to stay with Man and Boy by the ship to keep them safe.

Part 6. Aegreyan Assault

Once the characters escape Vuda's cave and return to *Three Hands Down*, they discover Man lying in the grass near the ship; he's dead. Looking over the coast some 500 feet away they see Qiu Xiang in a rowboat with Boy, who is unconscious. Another 1,500 feet from Qiu Xiang is an Aegreyan battleship. Before the characters can react to Qiu Xiang's betrayal, they see the dragon and griffon-riders headed for Grihoo Village.

Stopping Qiu Xiang

While it's possible to stop Qiu Xiang and save Boy, the characters are better off stopping the dragons and the Aegreyans. Qiu Xiang and Boy's story continues in the *The Hand of the Eight: Chapter 7 - The Summer Land,* found in *BroadSword Monthly #6.*

Addendum: Orner's Revenge Optional Subplot

Orner Wreros is a wildly intelligent gnomish inventor and wizard. His actions led to the crash of *The Predator* in the adventure *Titan's Heir: Chapter 1 - The Flight of the Predator, found in BroadSword Monthly #5.*

How to Use This Resource. This sub-plot contains events and actions of the NPC Orner Wreros that coincide with the main plot presented in the *Grihoo* adventure module. The content assumes that Wreros not only survived the crash of *The Predator* but is able to get away from the characters at some point during the adventure.

Each section of this resource identifies the actions Orner takes during each chapter of *Grihoo*. Some of the actions are taken "off-screen", and work as background information for you, the GM.

The Skeleton Key

At some point before the events of the *Grihoo* adventure module, Orner escapes into the forests. During his time in the forest, he discovers the remains of a Dinzer science vessel, *The Hyderabad*, that wrecked on the island a century ago. Within the hull of the vessel, Orner discovers a remote traveler juggernaut suit. As the characters struggle to survive the difficult conditions of the island, Orner starts rebuilding the suit. The only thing it's missing is a an emerald odonburgite core large enough to power it.

Chapter 1. Life Among the Serpent Whisperers

Shortly after the characters start their new life with the Serpent Whisperers on The Skeleton Key, Orner starts spying on the village. He eventually befriends Vuda, explaining that he was cast out of *The Predator* after the ship crashed. Recognizing Vuda's *firemind* condition, he claims that because he was "different" than the others, they treated him poorly. Vuda hides Orner in her cave.

Orner warns Vuda that the "greedy" characters might try to sabotage the village and that she must keep an eye on them at all times. Orner gives Vuda his goggles as a gift. Vuda, having never received a gift before, wears the goggles proudly.

Chapter 2. The Dying Light

When the lights go out, Vuda remembers what Orner told her. She believes that the characters had something to do with the pylons failing. She even says that "the small man told me something like this would happen!"

Defending Orner. At some point, the characters may decide to hunt for Orner. If they do, they can track Vuda back to her cave and find Orner there. Vuda confronts the characters with her tigers, explaining that they need to leave him alone. Because Vuda is a Serpent Whisperer, killing her is a crime punishable by death.

Vuda invokes an ancient Serpent Whisperer law—the Gift of Life. A Serpent Whisperer can protect another person or creature with the law that prevents killing Serpent Whisperers. A Serpent Whisperer may only grant this gift once in their entire life. If the characters kill Orner, they will be punished just as if they had killed a Serpent Whisperer.

Once Orner is protected by Vuda's Gift of Life, he joins her in the village and lives with the hunters. The hunters enjoy Orner's company and uphold Vuda's Gift of Life.

Chapter 3. Arrival

Orner witnesses the arrival of *Three Hands Down* and Barbakis' crew. Recognizing Dinzer technology, he knows that the ship carries an *emerald odonburgite* core. If he is in the village during the arrival, he asks to join the hunting party. Ykyope, not wanting to upset her sister, agrees.

After the combat with Orner and the others, Orner introduces himself to Theo Barbakis. Immediately, Orner recognizes Barbakis for what he is. When the others aren't around, Orner tells Barbakis that he will help him secure the village if Barbakis lets Orner take the emerald odonburgite. Barbakis agrees to the deal.

Chapter 4. Sabotage!

Following Orner's plan, Barbakis tricks Vuda into stealing the core from *Three Hands Down*. Vuda carries it to Orner who waits for her at her cave. Orner then attacks her with the stun pistol he discovered in *The Hyderabad's* wreckage and takes back

his goggles. With the core in hand, he flees back to *The Hyderabad*.

Chapter 5. Vuda and Her Cats

The characters discover Vuda in her cave. She remembers the creature who cast a spell on her and then Orner attacking her with his weapon. Hurt by Orner's betrayal, she pledges to help the characters defeat Orner.

Chapter 6. Aegreyan Assault

Instead of the characters facing off against Rain in the Moonlight and Vision in the Dark during the Aegreyan Assault, they must combat Orner in his **juggernaut** suit (see Appendix D for details). Orner, driven mad by his hatred for the characters, fights to the death this time.

Rain and Vision. When running the Orner's Revenge subplot, Rain and Vision instead appear in **area 3.01** of the Temple of Grihoo battling Sixty-six and Gar. Sixty-six is critical injured by the twins before the characters arrive.

Addendum: Grihoo Variant Endings

Part 8 of the *Grihoo* adventure module plays out with the characters battling Barbakis as he tries to steal power from the superhydra, Grihoo the Traveler. Depending on how weak or strong the characters are going into this final combat, you might substitute one of the following variant endings.

Both endings assume the characters find their way through Grihoo's labyrinth and discover Barbakis standing before the superhyrda.

Varant Ending: Grihoo Rises

In this low difficulty variant, the

characters come face to face with Theo Barbakis in his true, danaavrakt form. Read the following:

Although Barbakis is still wearing the Pressonian livery he wore when you met him, it's clear that he isn't human. His face looks like a tiger's, but the stripes of his fur writhe like a nest of snakes. Glowing red mist seeps out of his mouth when he speaks.

"Fools!" he declares! "You're too late!"

Ten feet behind Barbakis, a colossal ball of intertwined serpents each with a head the size of a horse's rises up and stares at you.

The fiend, Barbakis, cackles madly and raises his claws into the air.

"Soon, I will take the power of Grihoo the Traveler and with it, I shall rewrite all of existence!"

Barbakis turns to the superhydra.

"Grihoo! It is I! Your heir! Lend me your—"

In one swift move, three of the superhydra's heads bite Barbakis. Before the fiend can even shriek, he's torn apart into three uneven pieces and tossed in three different directions. No blood pours from Barbakis. Instead, his sections briefly glow with a red light and then vanish, leaving behind only the faint smell of sulfur.

Concluding the Adventure: Well, That Was Easy…

Give the characters a chance to react to seeing Barbakis easily destroyed by Grihoo. Before they can attack or flee, the temple starts to shake—it's about to explode!

The superhydra collects all of its heads before the characters. Its many eyes stare at the characters briefly before they all start to glow with black energy. Then, the flash of light from the temple's explosion washes over them and Grihoo disappears. When the light fades, the characters find themselves on a distant beach in the sun. In the distance, they see a city— Naqqad. They're back in Omeria. However, Grihoo, Barbakis, the island, and the temple are gone.

Varant Ending: Barbakis the Destroyer

In this high difficulty variant, the characters arrive just as Barbakis finishes taking Grihoo's power. Invigorated by the titan's energy coursing through his veins, Barbakis is more powerful than ever.

Read:

> Although Barbakis is still wearing the Pressonian livery he wore when you met him, it's clear that he isn't human. His face looks like a tiger's, but the stripes of his fur writhe like a nest of snakes. Glowing red mist seeps out of his mouth when he speaks. Black energy pulses around his clawed hands.
>
> "Yes," he hisses. "Its power is now mine."
>
> Ten feet behind Barbakis, a colossal ball of intertwined serpents each with a head the size of a horse's struggles to raise itself. Clearly, the fiend has done something to the beast.

Functionally, Barbakis is a **rakshasa**, but with the following changes:

Challenge Rating. Barbakis' has a CR 15 (13,000 XP).

New Action: Portal. Barbakis can use his action to create linked teleportation portals that remain open until the start of his next turn, until he uses the Portal action again, or until he uses his Redirect Projectile reaction. Barbakis chooses two points that he can see. Both points must be within 100 feet of him. A circular portal, 15 feet in diameter, opens over each point. The portals are two-dimensional glowing rings hovering in place and angled in any way Barbakis chooses. A ring is visible only from one side (Barbakis' choice), which is the side that functions as a portal.

If the portal would open in the space occupied by a creature, the creature must make a DC 18 Dexterity saving throw.

On a successful save, the creature can choose to move to a space within 5 feet of the portal. A creature that chooses not to move suffers the consequences of a failed saving throw.

On a failed saving throw, the creature falls through the portal.

Any creature or object entering the portal exits from the other portal as if the two were adjacent to each other, passing through a portal from the nonportal side has no effect. On Barabakis' turn, he can use his bonus action to extend the duration of the portal until the end of his next turn, or move one or both portals up to 30 feet and rotate them as he sees fit.

New Trait: Legendary Resistance (3/day). If Barbakis fails a saving throw, he can choose to succeed instead.

Legendary Actions. Barbakis can take 3 legendary actions, choosing from the options below. Only one legendary action can be used a time and only at the end of another creature's turn. Barbakis regains spent legendary actions at the start of his turn.

- **Attack.** Barbakis makes a claw attack.
- **Move.** Barbakis moves up to his full movement speed.
- **Frightening Gaze (Costs 2 Actions).** Barbakis fixes his gaze on one creature he can see within 10 feet of him. The target must succeed on a DC 18 Wisdom saving throw against this magic or become frightened for 1 minute. The frightened target can repeat the saving throw at the end of each of its turns, ending the effect on itself on a success. If a target's saving throw is successful or the effect ends for it, the target is immune ot Barbakis' gaze for the next 24 hours.
- **Portal (Costs 3 Actions).** Barbakis uses her Portal action.

Concluding the Adventure: Ouch

Barbakis in his improved form is not an easy fight. If it seems like he is close to defeating the party, just before he can destroy them all, Grihoo rises and uses the last of its power to teleport the characters away. The find themselves on a beach near Naqqad. Beyond the ocean, the characters witness a flash of light—the destruction of the island, the temple, and possibly Barbakis and Grihoo. Ω

ARTISTS SPOTLIGHT
THE ILLUSTRATORS OF BROADSWORD MONTHLY

BY SCOTT CRAIG
ART BY WILLIAM MCAUSLAND

BroadSword Monthly has been fortunate to have at its disposal some very talented illustrators and artists. Some pieces were specially commissioned, some purchased in collections for commercial use, while other works are readily available for free use thanks to generous patrons and artists.

In no particular order:

Sine Nomine Publishing

Kevin Crawford has released into the public domain select works from the following artists:

- David L. Johnson
  dlj.carbonmade.com
- Earl Geier
  www.freelanced.com/earlgeier
- Ian MacLean
  www.artstation.com/nvision
- Joyce Maureira
  http://www.joycemaureira.com
- Luigi Castellani
  www.patreon.com/artikid
- Miguel Santos
- Nate Furman
  www.deviantart.com/natefurman

Fat Goblin Games

"Publisher's Choice Quality Stock Art is copyright Rick Hershey / Fat Goblin Games"
www.fatgoblingames.com

Outland Arts

"Some artwork copyright William McAusland, used with permission."
www.outlandarts.com

Indie Conquest

Art released into the public domain by illustrator and game designer Jason Glover.
indieconquest.com

Bodie Hartley

Responsible for those cute monster illustration spreads and suchlike.
www.artstation.com/bodieh

Matias Lazaro

Entrusted with creating custom black and white scenes for DMDave's myriad adventures.
matiaslazaro.tumblr.com

The Griffon's Saddlebag

Member of Team Superhydra; item-crafter extraordinaire!
www.thegriffonssaddlebag.com

Paper Forge

Part of Team Superhydra; provides characterful PC & NPC illustrations.
www.patreon.com/paperforge

Cze and Peku

Members of Team Superhydra; provide highly detailed adventure locale combat maps.
www.patreon.com/czepeku

Dyson Logos

You know him, you love him, he's the master of daily dungeon mapping.
dysonlogos.blog

Watabou.itch.u

Creator of many interesting games and procedural generators!
www.patreon.com/watawatabou

Maps by Owen

Hand-drawn (with pen and ink!) fantasy maps.
www.mapsbyowen.com

Shutterstock

Home of random useful images.
www.shutterstock.com

Dean Spencer

"Some artwork © 2015 Dean Spencer, used with permission. All rights reserved."

Miska Fredman

Game designer and cartographer.
www.miskafredman.com

Maciej Zagorski

Graphic designer and illustrator.
www.behance.net/maciejzagorski Ω

ADVENTURES IN OMERIA

TALES OF OMERIA: PRIB'S PLOT

BY DAVE HAMRICK

1st-Level Adventure for Fifth Edition

Art by Matias Lazaro, Luigi Castellani and William McAusland.
Cartography by Meditating Munky

Prib's Plot is a Fifth Edition-compatible adventure for three to seven 1st to 3rd-level characters. The adventure is optimized for five characters with an average party level (APL) of 1. Characters who complete this adventure should earn enough XP to reach 2nd level.

The adventure takes place in The Contested Lands in DMDave's Omeria campaign. However, it can easily be inserted into any campaign world where a large town or city sits at the edge of a large desert.

Adventure Background

The town of Musfarah sits on the banks of the River Midnight roughly 50 miles south of city-state Naqqad, to which its people owe their allegiance. Originally, the town acted as a trade port along the river and the Tears of Karnione. In recent years it's had to pivot to be a fortress town as the civil war that rages between Dorithell, Ingum, Nadorith, and Naqqad enters its twelfth year.

Musfarah is operated by Amir Aslani, a general known for his kind demeanor and wisdom. Unusual for a lifelong soldier, Aslani has helped Musfarah avoid unnecessary conflicts through diplomacy and negotiation with the opposition.

Starting a few weeks ago, Aslani began acting strange. He showed up to meetings late, drunk and belligerent. He turned his attention away from his duties and toward women and wine. When new conflicts arose, Aslani addressed the Musfarahnian concerns with apathy. "If we die, we die."

Some believe that Aslani's sudden change in attitude is the result of stress typical for soldiers with his responsibilities. Others suspect he came under the spell of some wicked spellcaster who hopes to weaken Musfarah's defenses.

Whatever is causing Aslani's breakdown, the town elders want to know if there is anything they can do to remedy it. While it's possible to supplant Aslani with new leadership, the elders fear that a sudden change in command this late in the game could display weakness. This would hamper Musfarah's diplomatic relations with Naqqad's enemies and make the town a tantalizing target in the eyes of the opposition.

Adventure Hook

The characters find themselves in the Naqqadi town of Musfarah. The reasons that they are there are up to you. But they might be winding down from a recent adventure in the area or they might have been invited there from a close ally.

At some point, the characters come into contact with Azadeh Rostami, one of Musfarah's elders. If the characters aren't known for their exploits, Rostami knows of the characters through a friend of a friend. Or, the characters could hear rumors that Rostami seeks assistance with a local issue.

Rostami explains to the characters that something unusual is happening with the town's leader, General Amir Aslani. She offers the details explained in the Background section of this module. One of Rostami's spies learned that Aslani left the town two days ago, heading west through the desert on a camel. This is not the first time he's left the town. In fact, the first time he vanished like this was just before he started to act strange.

Rostami requests that the characters follow the general and learn his whereabouts. She offers the characters 500 gp for any information they can bring back regarding the General. She also shares that if there is anything they can do to help the General and relieve him of his unusual state the town of Musfarah will forever be in their debt.

Tracking General Aslani. Aslani's path is a couple days old when the characters start on their mission. A character can pick up his trail by making a successful DC 15 Wisdom (Survival) check. After 8 hours of travel, the camel's prints lead to an old temple in the desert.

If the characters fail to pick up Aslani's trail, they can attempt to find the general again the following day. At your discretion, they might pass a desert nomad or wanderer who saw the general pass through. The nomad offers directions to the temple where they saw the general heading.

The Temple of Jaojian

Long ago, during the times of Karnione, the desertfolk who claimed the lands west of Naqqad built a grand temple to the efreet, Uve the Harrow. A cleric named Jaojian oversaw the temple's operations. Following Uve's destruction in the mid-9th century, Jaojian and the other desertfolk abandoned the temple and the desert reclaimed it.

A year ago, a pesky desert satyr named Prib Purplemouth discovered the temple and reclaimed it, restoring it to its former glory. Prib then filled it with other creatures that shared the same chaotic bent as he.

Two weeks ago, General Amir Aslani happened upon the temple while on a sabbatical. Prib, recognizing the general, used his panpipes to coax the general into the temple. Within, the general partook in Prib's luxurious parties and celebrations. After two days, the general emerged enchanted by the satyr's lifestyle. Addicted to Prib's way of life, the general returned to Musfarah a changed man.

When the characters arrive at the Temple of Joajian, the general has already decided that he will spend the rest of his days there with Prib and Prib's friends.

General Features

The temple's walls, ceilings, and floors are made from huge limestone blocks that were laid by the giants who once shared the temple with the desertfolk. The walls are carved with elaborate arabesque and calligraphic patterns of the old Karnionic language.

The ceilings soar 50-feet over chambers and 15-feet over corridors. The temple possesses multiple domes of varying conditions, the majority of which are made from baked and carved brick.

The temple's impressive wooden doors are set into 8- to 12-foot stone arches and set on steel hinges. The

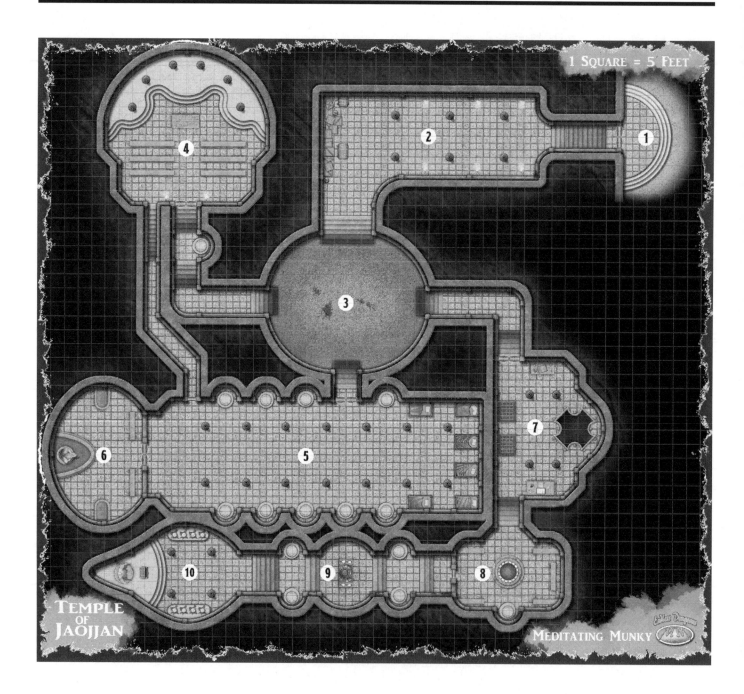

TEMPLE OF JAOJJAN

MEDITATING MUNKY

doors all have internal locks. When locked, a creature with proficiency in thieves' tools can pick the lock with a successful DC 13 Dexterity check. Alternatively, a door can be broken down with a successful DC 15 Strength check.

Torches and large braziers are kept magically lit by *continual flame* spells throughout the complex.

Keyed Locations

The following locations are keyed to the map of the temple on this page.

1 - Temple Entrance
When the characters first arrive, read the following:

> This old temple is half buried under the desert's hungry sands. A camel stands tethered to a nearby

rock, quietly watching you. Humanoid footprints lead away from the camel to a set of 12-foot high wooden double doors at the front of the temple.

The tracks are the general's. The doors are unlocked.

2 - Entry Hall
Once the doors are opened, read the following:

When you open the doors, the first thing you notice is soft music playing somewhere in the distance. There is perfume in the air.

A staircase rises to a higher level. From where you stand you see the warm glow of fire light dancing on the ornate walls of this desert temple.

At the top of the stairs, the characters find a long hallway with two rows of columns on either side of the path. Braziers cast bright light throughout the entire area.

Encounter: Revelers. Three revelers are dancing in the hallway, while a fourth plays a lyre and sings (treat them as CN **nobles**). The revelers are friendly, but only interested in unbridled hedonism. The four have been tasked to stop anyone who enters the temple and learn their intentions. If they are attacked, they fight back, giggling and laughing as they do. They are all drunk, which gives them the poisoned condition. Even if they are harmed, they jest at their own wounds. Otherwise, the group is harmless.

The revelers were traders who became enthralled by Prib's presence. The two men are named Mojtaba and Sina, and the two women are named Atefah and Dorsa. Dorsa is the musician.

Treasure. Barrels and crates crowd the far, western edge of the room. The crates are filled with food and bottles of wine, and the barrels are filled with ale. These are goods the traders offered Prib. Altogether, there is 2,000 pounds worth of trade goods. All of the trade goods are worth 200 gp at the market.

3 - Earthen Room

This large room lacks the same tile floors you've encountered so far throughout the rest of this old desert temple. In its place, is the raw earth. One hundred feet above you,

a great brick dome protects this area from the elements.

A woman lies at the center of this earthen courtyard. She laughs hysterically, taking swigs from a bottle as she does. She raises her empty hand to you—it's turned to stone. "Look!" she laughs, "It gave me a kiss!"

You watch as she takes another sip from her bottle, her entire body turning to stone as she does. Just behind her, a three-foot tall creature that resembles a chicken covered in reptilian scales clucks at you.

This area lacks its own light sources. Only the dim light cast by the side passages gives the characters a view of what is in this room.

Encounter: Cockatrice. The creature that "kissed" the woman was a **cockatrice**. It won't hesitate to attack the characters, but flees if it's hit points are reduced by half or more.

Petrified Bodies. Four more revelers were turned to stone by the cockatrice, each one frozen in laughter. Their bodies lie about this area. They all return to their normal forms within 24 hours; they are all **commoners**.

4 - Chapel

This grand chapel features a large, stone altar near its center. Two rows of stone benches face the altar. Two drunken revelers lie on the benches, snoring loudly.

Beyond the altar a stone dais upon which six columns stand in a semicircle dominates the north part of the room.

All of the room's surfaces are lightly dusted with sand.

The revelers are both commoners. They were enchanted by the chapel's sleeping sands.

Hazard: Sleeping Sands. The sand is imbued with residual elemental magic. When the characters enter this

room, the sand starts to swirl through the area. Each character must make a DC 10 Constitution saving throw, or fall unconscious for 1 hour as per the *sleep* spell. The only way to rid the area of the hazard is to gather all the sand and cast *dispel magic* upon it, a daunting task to be sure.

5 - Makeshift Barracks

This large area looks like it was once a grand antechamber. Now, it appears to be the epicenter of hedonism and celebration at the center of the temple. Dozens of humanoids wearing little more than sheets draped over their lithe forms dance, drink, and sing.

In the center of the chaos, a creature covered in fur dances and plays a pan flute. The creature has the legs and horns of a goat, but the face of a man.

Encounter: Prib and His Followers. There are twenty-four **commoners** dancing with Prib, the **satyr**. When the characters enter the room, Prib is already playing his pipes. If the characters are within 60 feet of Prib and can hear the pipes, they must succeed on a DC 13 Wisdom saving throw or be affected by Prib's charming melody. The character is charmed by Prib for 1 minute. If Prib or any of its companions harms the character, the effect on them ends immediately.

A character affected in this way can repeat its saving throw at the end of each of its turns, ending the effect on themselves with a success. If the character's saving throw is successful or the effect ends for it, the character is immune to Prib's panpipes for 24 hours.

If the characters avoid being charmed by Prib and act hostile, Prib hides among his throng of followers. The revelers are unarmed (they make attack rolls with a +0 to hit and only deal 1 bludgeoning damage on a hit).

Most will try to subdue and grapple the characters.

If Prib is pressed, he puts his panpipes away and switches to his short bow, using the columns as cover. If the characters reduce Prib's hit points by half or fewer, he attempts to surrender, offering them anything he has at his disposal, including the sack of gold coins he keeps hidden in **area 6**.

Prib offers that General Amir Aslani is in the westernmost chamber (**area 5**). However, he warns the characters that he's drunk and looking for a fight. If the characters accuse Prib of enchanting the general, he explains that while the General may have been enchanted by his pipes the first time they met, no spell forced the General to return to the temple this time.

If the characters leave Prib be, he and the other revelers continue their celebration into the night (and likely beyond).

6 - Water Chapel

> The western end of this room features a large water basin upon which a statue carved to resemble a maiden sits at the center.

Prib uses this room to get away from the other revelers and to sleep. The water comes from an underground spring and is safe to drink.

Encounter: General Amir Aslani. General Aslani (N male human **knight**) is here and he's drunk; treat him as being under the effects of the poisoned condition. And just as Prib said, he is not under any sort of enchantment. When Aslani met Prib, he was already having a crisis of faith. Aslani wanted to escape the burdens of leadership. Prib and his revelers offered a window for him to do just that.

If the characters spend 10 minutes or longer talking with Aslani, a successful DC 10 Wisdom (Insight) check reveals that Aslani might come to his senses if the characters remind him that the future of Musfarah and its people are at stake. Once they suggest just that, have one or more characters make a Charisma (Persuasion) check contested by Aslani's Wisdom (Insight) check. On a success, Aslani agrees to return to Musfarah and resume his duties. Otherwise, he rejects his leadership role and continues to stay with Prib and the others, assuming Prib is still alive.

If the characters try to fight with Aslani, he only fights them long enough to prove that he can best them. If the characters kill Aslani, that likely creates an interesting predicament for them and the people of Musfarah.

Treasure. A character who makes a successful DC 13 Intelligence (In-

vestigation) near the water finds a coin pouch at the basin's bottom. The sack contains 100 gp. Prib stored his coins here to keep the revelers from stealing them (sure, the revelers are charmed by him, but that doesn't mean they won't steal from him).

7 - Door to The Other

The doors leading to this chamber from **area 3** are locked. Written across the door are the words "Danger! Do not enter!" in Common.

The first time that the characters enter this room, read the following:

> There is a strong smell of burning leather in this room. At the west end of the room sits a basin with painted purple edges. No water sits in the basin, but instead, within swirls dark fog.
>
> Against the western wall of the room stand two cages from which a pair of skeletons grin back at you.

The ceilings in this room are 30-feet high. The basin is a one-way portal to The Other, an endless realm of shadow. Only creatures from The Other can use the portal. It activates when a living creature touches it.

Cages. The two cages are locked. There is nothing of value within either cage.

Encounter: Shadows. If any of the characters touch the edge of the basin with their flesh, two **shadows** emerge from the fog and attack.

Treasure. At the north end of the room stands an altar, upon it which lies a spellbook. The spellbook contains the following wizard spells: 1st—*false life*; 2nd—*gentle repose*; 3rd—*animate dead*. There is also a dagger. The dagger exudes magic from the school of necromancy. However, it is cursed, and activates when one of the characters attunes to it. Until the curse is removed, undead creatures have advantage on attacks made against the character.

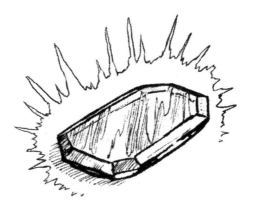

8 - Emerald Odonburgite

> At the center of this large room there is a large, stone basin within which a massive green gem sits.

Emerald Odonburgite Gem. The gem was once an extremely large piece of emerald Odonburgite (see Appendix C), a magical gem capable of powering magic items. The gem lost all its energy years ago.

If the characters can find a way to remove and transport the ten ton gem, it's worth 1,000 gp to someone who understands its value.

Otherwise, there is nothing else of value in this area.

9 - Scrying Pool

> At the center of this room stands a stone table. Upon the table sit two masks, four empty potion bottles, and a bowl in which green liquid stands. The masks are split down the middle, with black on one side and white on the other.

The bowl of green liquid was once used to scry, but no longer functions. The masks have no function, and the potions are empty.

Treasure. A character who searches the pedestal and succeeds on a DC 15 Intelligence (Investigation) check finds a long and narrow secret compartment. Inside the compartment,

they will find a maul covered in dried blood. The maul is exquisitely crafted and worth 50 gp.

10 - Room of Flowers

> At both the north and south sides of this room stand two tables dressed with purple flowers. At the west end of the room stands a stone statue of a large humanoid. At the statue's feet sit a wooden chest, its lid open.

The treasure chest is empty, its contents removed years ago. The flowers are magically enchanted to never die. If removed from the temple, they instantly wither away.

Statue of Uve. A successful DC 13 Intelligence (Religion) check reveals that the statue depicts Uve, a powerful efreet, once worshipped by the founders of this temple.

If a character searches the statue, on a successful DC 15 Intelligence (Investigation) check they discover a piece of rolled up parchment. The parchment details the blueprints of a large palace. At the center of the place, hidden behind a statue, is a secret staircase that leads downward. An arrow points to the staircase with the words "his ring is here" scrawled in the Ignan language.

Concluding the Adventure: Return of the General

If the characters successfully convince General Amir Aslani to return to Musfarah, the general reclaims his role as leader and within a week recognizes the importance of his position. However, if the characters failed, Musfarah descends into chaos as Musfarah's lieutenants vie for the general's position as the town's leader. Such a collapse in faith brings greater trouble as word spreads of the general's departure. The characters might find themselves at the middle of a war. Ω

TALES OF OMERIA: CHORUS OF TOADS

BY DAVE HAMRICK

5th-Level Adventure for Fifth Edition

Art by Matias Lazaro, Maciej Zagorski, and William McAusland
Cartography by Dyson Logos

This side trek is designed for two to three 5th- to 7th-level characters and is optimized for two characters with an average party level (APL) of 5. It especially works well when half of your normal campaign group can't show up and there are two or three players who still want to play.

Chorus of Toads is a horror story that takes liberties with one or more absent players' characters. Before running the adventure, be sure to ask the players of the absent characters if you can "borrow" their characters for the adventure. Feel free to provide details described within the text. Unless the participating characters cause an absolute disaster, the absent characters should be fine by the end of this adventure.

Adventure Background

Eighty years ago, the village of Tenellón was founded ten miles north of Uqamarte. Tenellón is surrounded on all sides by thick salt marshes with few trees. The only way into the hamlet of thirty-some inhabitants is via a narrow path that is known to flood over during the wet season. Like many of the towns and villages in the Lost Dragon pass, Tenellón owes taxes to Arruquetta. In exchange, it is awarded a single Cord, one of Arruquetta's not-so-secret police force, who keeps watch over the area. Tenellón hunters trade frogs, alligator pelts and birds with other local villages. Most Weysevainers who happen upon the quiet village consider the Tenellónians to be quaint, pleasant folks, who would never harm a single hair on another creature's head.

Adventure Overview

The adventure is spread out over five parts.

- *Introduction: The Gargoyle's Smile.* The characters discover that their companions have gone missing.
- *Part 1. The Bald Swamp and*

Toad Chorus Way. Tracking their allies, the characters arrive at a tourist destination in the middle of the swamp. There, they speak to a strange man named Hedoi.

- *Part 2. Tenellón*. The characters learn that their companions went to the village of Tenellón. They must travel to Tenellón and speak with the villagers..

- *Part 3. Guidon's Tower*. The characters travel outside of the village to Guidon's Tower. While there, they are attacked. Soon they discover that their friends were captured by dangerous creatures that live in the swamp.

- *Part 4. Return to Tenellón*. Having saved their friends, the characters return to the village of Tenellón. They discover that the villagers all share a dark secret.

Adventure Hook: Gone Adventuring! Back Later!

At some point between the last adventure and now, one or more of the party members have gone missing. They went to investigate a tourist attraction and were supposed to return after a few hours. It's been a whole day and there's still no sign of them.

The remaining adventurers must follow a series of clues as to where their fellow party members vanished. Eventually, this leads them to the quiet hamlet of Tenellón.

Intro: The Gargoyle's Smile

The adventure assumes that the characters are in the northwestern part of Central Omeria, specifically on the well-traveled road, The Leash. The Leash connects the four major cities of the Weysevain Coast. While traveling along The Leash, the characters stay at The Gargoyle's Smile, a popular tavern and inn. The Smile is a two days ride from the town of Uqamarte. The characters have had a terrific time unwinding and enjoying themselves after finishing up an adventure in the area.

The next morning, one or more members of the party heard a rumor of a strange blue rock a few miles north of the tavern. The tavernkeepers at The Smile claim it's a big tourist attraction that draws a lot of outsiders. "Looks like a big diamond stuck in the mud, I hear."

To reach the stone, visitors must turn west off The Leash onto a trail called Toad Chorus Way. A half-hour walk up the trail takes travelers to a shack where the guide can escort them to the diamond.

Eight hours pass and the other characters still haven't returned. It's now up to the remaining characters to find out what happened to their companions.

Part 1. The Bald Swamp and Toad Chorus Way

It only takes a half-hour to find Toad Chorus Way and another half-hour to find the shack that the tavernkeepers described.

Area Description

The Bald Swamp has the following features:

Dimensions & Terrain. The Bald Swamp is a 2,200 square mile stretch of soggy landscape with little to no trees. Instead, small shrubs, bushes, and tall grasses claim the area.

Divination Interference. The presence of *vizier's tourmaline* (see Appendix C) in the area distorts divination magic. When a creature casts a divination spell in The Bald Swamp, it must make an Intelligence (Arcana) check with a DC equal to 10 + the spell's level. On a failed check, the spell fails and has no effect just as if it had been the target of a *counterspell*. Also, creatures with truesight have their ranges reduced by half.

Insects. Mosquitoes are a plague in the swamp. At the end of each hour that a character spends in and around the swamp, they must make a DC 10 Constitution saving throw. On a failed saving throw, the character has disadvantage on ability checks until the end of the next hour. On a successful saving throw, a character is immune to the mosquitoes for 24 hours. Rangers and characters with the outlander background automatically pass their saving throws.

Smells. Thanks to the brown, stagnant water that drowns the floor of the swamp, The Bald Swamp reeks.

Sounds. The Bald Swamp is alive with insects, birds, and of course, frogs and toads. At night, the toads in

The Bald Swamp reach near-deafening levels with their croaks.

The Blue Diamond Shack

The Blue Diamond Shack is a lean-to on stilts sitting atop a marginally higher dry patch of ground. The front of the shack lacks a wall—there's only a five-foot-long counter topped with wicker baskets. A big sign painted in blue letters reads "Come See The Great Blue Diamond!" in the Common language. It then gives prices: 1 gp for a tour, 4 sp for a basket (or buy 3 for 10 sp).

When the shack's owner, Hedoi, isn't sitting up front weaving reed baskets, he's in the back of the shack sleeping, cooking dinner, or playing his flute.

Creature Information

Hedoi is a friendly, older human with balding hair and a sunburnt nose. As soon as he sees travelers coming down the path, he rings a bell that he keeps hanging above his counter with cries of "Welcome! Welcome!"

What Does Hedoi Want? Hedoi loves to regale folks with tales of the diamond as big as a horse in the mud north of his shack. If he can't sell you on a tour, he'll make sure you leave with a basket or two (or three).

What Does Hedoi Know? If the characters ask about their companions, Hedoi thinks for a moment explaining that his memory isn't what it used to be. Once he's given a complete description of them, however, he remembers immediately.

> "Oh yes! Yes yes yes. I do remember! They done gone off with Ms Maria up to Tenellón. She told 'em she runned into a whole heap of trouble down there and needed their help."

Hedoi is telling the truth. Last he saw the other characters, they were traveling with a woman named Maria to the village of Tenellón and Maria told them she was in trouble. Hedoi claims not to know much more than

that but will try to be as helpful as he can. As far as directions go, it's only 2 miles (a half-hour walk) from his shack to Tenellón.

The Great Blue Diamond. If the characters take Hedoi up on his offer to see the diamond, he gladly leads them to its location through the swamp. The "diamond" in question is about 1,000 feet behind his shack. The diamond turns out to not be a diamond at all. Instead, it's just a large piece of glass stuck in the mud. Hedoi isn't sure where it came from, but a character who succeeds on a successful DC 13 Intelligence (Arcana) check might recognize that it's the result of a *fireball* spell turning a sandbar into glass. Whoever did it likely did it 15-20 years ago. Either way, Hedoi is proud of it. The man claims that it's the reason some spells don't work as well as others in the swamp.

> "Wheeewww-wee! Sure is a beaut, ain't it?"

Part 2. Tenellón

The village of Tenellón is easy to find. And with very few trees to block views of the village, the characters can spot it when they're within a half-mile.

Area Description

The village of Tenellón has the following features:

Dimensions & Terrain. Tenellón is a hamlet home to thirty-two swamp-dwelling people. There are only seven buildings in Tenellón. Six of the buildings are residential homes and the seventh is an old wizard's tower roughly 700-feet from the edge of the hamlet. Toad Chorus Way passes through the village and ends at the tower. The six residential homes are built on stilts to account for rising waters during the wet season.

Animals. The livestock that the Tenellónians trade for with other Weysevanian villages are kept in plain view, often tied to stakes on the ground. There are goats, chickens, and pigs. There are also dozens of stacked crates packed with croaking toads.

Light. The Tenellónians keep lanterns hung in front of each of their homes. At night, the lamplighter Philippe keeps the village illuminated. And in the morning, Phillippe wakes early to extinguish the flames and replenish the oil.

Mud. Mud is a way of life for Tenellónians, and it's everywhere, including inside houses. Most Tenellónians wear thigh-high leather boots to avoid getting their feet wet. Others choose to go the other route, forgoing shoes altogether and wearing little more than denim pants cut just below the groin.

Creature Information

The Tenellónians are incredibly friendly and welcoming. Right away, they're interested in trade and any news that the characters might have.

When asked questions, they're eager to answer as soon as they are able.

What Do The Tenellónians Know? If asked about the missing characters, the Tenellónians immediately remember. Most can share their account of the story: Maria was traveling to The Gargoyle's Smile to find an adventurer. Apparently, some sort of Toad-like creature was seen north of the town. While the Tenellónians are able hunters, they aren't cut out for fighting monsters. And the town's Cord, Guy, hasn't been seen in a few days. Maria led the characters to Guimond's Tower—the dilapidated tower 700-feet north of the hamlet.

Important Tenellónians

The Tenellónians are divided into six families: Adunibar, Alonso, Enatarreaga, Harrizurieta, Marien, and Urquina.

- **Maria** comes from the Urquina family. She's one of eight children.
- Maria's father is the hamlet's mayor, **Laponte Urquina**. He often rubs those he meets the wrong way, but overall, he's cooperative.
- **Phillipe Harrizurieta** is the town's lamplighter and frog-catcher. Phillipe is in love with Maria and fears for her life. He laments that he is not as brave as most heroes, but will offer to accompany the characters if it means he can save his true love's life.
- **Old Man Lilo Enatarreaga** often barks that the entire village is doomed. "It's the old curse!" he claims. Enatarreaga believes that the village is cursed because of a murder that happened in the swamps 20 years ago.
- Enatarreaga's daughter, **Oketa**, stays by her father's side. She apologizes for his outbursts. "Sadly, he's just gotten more and more delirious as the years have gone by." She doesn't know anything about the curse of the murder.
- **Mañe Adunibar** is a teenage girl who tries to get the attention of the

characters the moment they step in town. She warns, "You can't trust anyone." When out of earshot of her fellow villagers, she explains, "I don't know who's responsible for it, but 20 years ago someone got murdered here and some of the folks in this village are still trying to cover it up. I think your friends got close to finding out who it was. They went up to the tower and didn't come back."
- **Andrianos Perras** is a Pressonian biologist who has been camping in the village. He and his companion, **Yorgos**, came to The Bald Swamp two months ago to study the fabled "Toad Man" of The Bald Swamp. Although they keep hearing reports of the creature near Guimond Tower, they have yet to see it with their own eyes.

Part 3. Guimond's Tower

Eventually, the characters should go to investigate the old tower north of the village.

Area Description

Guimond's Tower has the following features:

Dimensions & Terrain. The octagonal tower is made from the same thick stone upon which it stands. The villagers believe that a transmuter wizard named Guimond built the tower, pulling the stones up from the earth itself. Whether or not that is true, The Bald Swamp and the pounding rains of the Weysevain Coast haven't been kind to the building. Much of the building's east side is crumbling and the wooden dome roof has collapsed in multiple places.

Clues. When the characters approach the tower, right away they notice something unusual. Roughly 30 feet from the base of the tower, a torn piece of fabric, trinket, or some other identifying item of one of their companions lies in the grass by the tower. A DC 10 Intelligence (Investigation) check reveals that the item

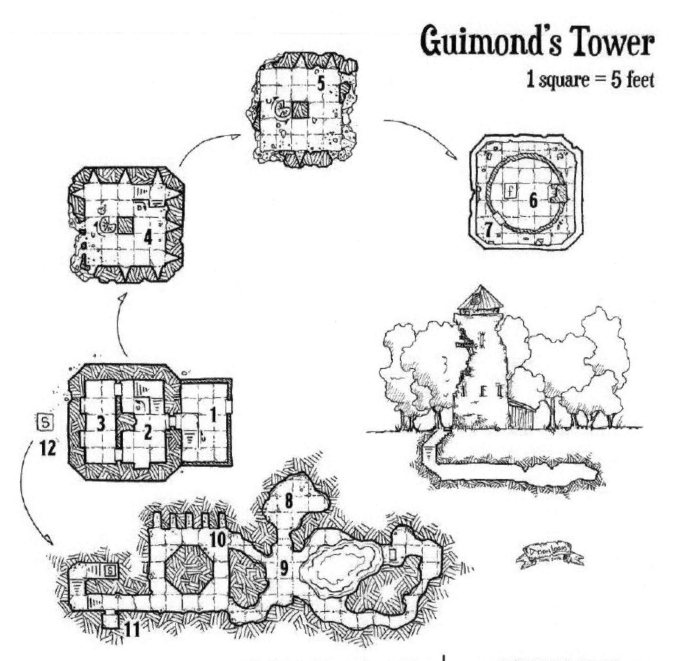

Guimond's Tower

1 square = 5 feet

SUPPORTED ON PATREON | www.DYSONLOGOS.com

was torn away.

Footprints. There are multiple sets of footprints in the mud that lead to the tower (**area 1**). A DC 12 Wisdom (Survival) check reveals that it is the footprints of the character's companions plus one other set of small, humanoid footprints (likely Maria's).

Toads. Hundreds of toads litter the grounds around the tower. The toads

are harmless. It just takes a little effort to walk around the tower and not step on them.

Keyed Locations

1 - Entrance
The eastern end of the tower is a lean-to shack built against the stone base. The old, wooden front door is so

warped it won't even latch anymore. The muddy footprints enter the area and head straight toward **area 2**.

2 - Stairs
An old, mildew-covered couch sits against the southern wall. The muddy footprints continue up the stairs to **area 4**.

3 - Dining Room

An old dining table takes up the majority of this room. The chairs that once surrounded it are either broken and rotting or long-since stolen. The room reeks of rot.

4 - Library

Dozens of empty, crumbling shelves line the walls. There is a massive hole in the western wall exposing this area to the elements. If there were ever books in this area, they're long gone. The muddy footprints continue up the stairs to **area 5**.

5 - Ruined Area

It's impossible to tell what this room once was. Most of the walls have been torn away by years of neglect. The muddy footprints continue up the stairs to **area 6**.

6 - Room

Finally, the footprints reach the top of the tower. The walls of this circular room are made of wood. There is an old bed covered in mildew and insects against the northern wall. An old, crumbling fireplace clings to the eastern wall. The footprints continue out the door to **area 7**.

7 - View

The top of the tower gives a breathtaking view of The Bald Swamp. The footprints move around the edge of the tower to its northeastern side then suddenly end.

Maria. If a character looks over the edge of the tower's balcony (**area 7**), they see a body lying in the grass 30 feet from the north side of the tower. The body appears to be a young woman in her early twenties with long, blonde hair. She matches the description of Maria. A character who succeeds on a DC 15 Wisdom (Perception) check can see that she is still breathing.

Maria is not actually Maria—she's a silent image illusion cast on the grass patch. Noticing that Maria is an illusion requires a DC 13 Intelligence (Investigation) check. Unfortunately, a character must get close enough to observe her. Maria's illusion is cast over a 5-foot-by-5-foot hidden trap door in the ground. A successful DC 15 Intelligence (Investigation) check is necessary to confirm that the trapped section of the ground is actually the cover of a pit trap.

When a character steps onto the cover, it swings open like a trapdoor, causing the character to spill into a chute. After 20-feet, the chute buckles at a 45-degree angle and spits out the character into **area 8**. The character takes no damage from the fall, but lands prone.

Creature Information. If the characters see through the trap, then the creatures who set the trap reveal themselves. Two toad-humanoid hybrids attack, rising from the murky water a few feet from where the characters stand. The creatures are **bufonems** (see Appendix D).

What Do They Want? The bufonems hoped to capture the characters in their trap so they could deal with them later. When Maria is revealed as an illusion, they react quickly to cover their tracks by attacking the characters. Their goal is to still get the characters into the cell in **area 8**. Failing that, they try to murder the characters.

What Do They Know? The bufonems captured the characters' friends and stowed them in the jail cell in **area 8**. Only their master knows what has happened to them since they were captured. The creatures will try their best to avoid any other questions asked by the characters, but do know enough about the tower, the characters, and the village to reveal the heart of Tenellón's mystery.

8 - Cell

The "Maria Trap" deposits intruders into this damp cavern.

Area Description. The cell has the following features:

Dimensions & Terrain. The cell is roughly 15-feet by 15-feet. The walls, floor, and ceiling are made from slick, hewn stone. The only exit is a locked cage door in the southern part of the cell. The chute's portal is in the ceiling of the cell.

Body. The bloated, rotting corpse of a dead doppelganger sits in the mud of the cell floor. It is wearing a black, dark blue, and fuschia uniform. A character who makes a successful DC 10 Intelligence (History) check recognizes it as the body of a Cord, one of Arruquetta's secret police. The doppelganger has a knife wound in its ribcage and lacerations around its neck from a bufonem's tongue.

Cage Door. The cage door is made out of crisscrossing iron bars. Only the master bufonem has the key. The door can be broken down with a successful DC 20 Strength (Athletics) check or its lock can be picked with a successful DC 15 Dexterity check by a character who has proficiency in thieves' tools. There are marks around the door's hinges that suggest that the door has recently been replaced.

Light. Like the rest of the caverns under the tower, the cell is dark.

Chute. The chute which deposits creatures into the cell is often slick with mud. It requires a DC 20 Strength (Athletics) check for a character to climb up. Then, they must get the trapdoor open, which requires an additional DC 15 Strength (Athletics) check. Failing either check forces a character to fall back into the cell.

9 - The Den

The bufonem gather in this chamber to tend to their young and eat the captured prisoners that they don't sacrifice to Dhucabra.

Area Description. The den has the following features:

Dimensions & Terrain. The ceilings of this dark stone cavern are low, generally no higher than 10-feet.

Everything is wet to the touch. The ground, while flat, is just hewn stone.

Altar. Just beyond the pool, a crud altar made of blood-stained humanoid bones has been erected. Atop the altar sits a hunk of dimly glowing red rock. The rock is *ruby blutvekzelnite* (see Appendix C).

Pool. A murky, green pool covers the floor of the majority of this cavern. Hundreds of translucent bufonem eggs float on the surface of the water.

Tunnels. Multiple tunnels lead in and out of the den. The bufonems use these tunnels to stage surprise attacks on their prey.

Creature Information. The characters quickly learn they aren't alone. Using the tunnels and their knowledge of the layout to their advantage, four **bufonem** (see Appendix D) seek to subdue the characters.

10 - The Bleeding Chamber
This area is directly below the tower above.

Area Description. The Bleeding Chamber has the following features:

Dimensions & Terrain. At the center of the room is a solid, stone octagon that supports the weight of Guidon's Tower. The ceilings are low here, too, only 10-feet.

Alcoves. There are five narrow cubbies dug into the northern wall. The alcoves contain:

- The missing characters; each character is unconscious and his/her hit points are reduced to 1.
- A dead human.

Each of the captive's arms are bound above his or her head. All of their belongings have been removed, and if any of them are a spellcaster, their mouth has been sewn shut as well. Finally, dozens of small cuts have been made all over their bodies.

Blood. Blood drains from the alcoves' victims to the octagon at the center of the room.

Blue Gems. At regular intervals, small, blue gems have been placed into alcoves dug into the octagon.

The gems are small pieces of *vizier's tourmaline* (see Appendix C). The ambient energy of the gems have kept the Tenellón hidden from those who would persecute them.

The identities of the other dead humans are up to you, but likely, they were travelers who wandered into Tenellón and were attacked by the toadfolk.

11 - Storage
All of the missing characters' possessions are stored in this 5-foot by 5-foot chamber.

12 - Exit
A flight of steps leads out of the tower's secret basement to the rear of the tower. From the outside, the trapdoor is hidden. It requires a DC

15 Intelligence (Investigation) check to discover it.

Part 4. Back to Tenellón
When the characters return to Tenellón it appears that there is no one around. No children playing, no hunters chatting. There is only the sound of the swamp and the animals. But slowly as the characters move along the Toad Chorus Path they start to notice creatures moving out of the corner of their eyes.

Eventually, they realize that every single living soul in Tenellón is a **bufonem**. The mayor, the children, even the crazy old man—all of them are horrible toadfolk.

There are thirty-two of the toad-folk minus one for each one the characters killed or otherwise incapacitated at the tower.

> "For eighty years," croaks one of the townsfolk, their features distorting and changing before your very eyes. They transform into a seven-foot-tall toad-humanoid with three, bulbous yellow eyes. Their wide mouths reveal sharp, red teeth "We have hidden. And we have lived. But with the blood of the dulon's final creation we will find a path to the lost titan."
>
> All of the toad-creatures—formerly the villagers—chant in unison, "Dhucabra... Dhucabra... Dhucabra..."
>
> They start to close in on you.

If the characters are wise, they will run from the village. This may involve a chase (see the rules for Wilderness Chases in Chapter 8 of the *DMG*). However, if they lack the common sense to flee from such a difficult encounter, the toadfolk have no interest in killing them. Instead, they plan to knock the characters unconscious. If all of the characters are knocked unconscious, they awaken to the sound of battle.

Read:

You wake to the smell of smoke and the warmth of fire on your skin. All around you, stand soldiers in black, navy blue, and fuschia uniforms. The village of Tenellón is in flames. Among the soldiers is a Southern Omerian warrior wearing a lion's pelt over her shoulders. Four of the soldiers hold one of the toadfolk by its arms and allow the Southern Omerian to run the beast through with her spear. The creature shrieks and dies.

Little did the characters know, the Arruquettans had been watching Tenellón for some time. Their Southern Omerian comrade, a witchhunter from the land of Aspaeth named Noma, believed the village might be a hideout for the fiendish toads of Aspaeth. Turns out her premonition was correct. Shortly after the characters left Hedoi's shack, the Arruquettans captured Hedoi and discovered that he, too, was a **bufonem** (see Appendix D). Although Hedoi wouldn't reveal the true nature of Tenellón to the Cords, Noma put two and two together. She killed Hedoi then immediately marched to the village with an elite unit of Cords.

"We killed seven of them. The rest vanished into the swamp. They won't get far."

The Southern Omerian warrior holds up a blue gem.

"Smart. They were using *vizier's tourmaline* to hide their presence. But they could have lived here in peace forever had they just kept to themselves. Why risk it all?"

They Were Toads!

Astute readers may have noticed that the stat references for the villagers were largely absent during the adventure. This was intentional. The story is designed to surprise GMs reading it for the first time so they can share the shock with their players.

Yes, all of the villagers in Tenellón were **bufonems** disguised as humans.

Concluding the Adventure: Dhucabra

The captured characters remember very little of the encounter. Maria escorted the characters back to the village and then to the tower to handle the "toad creature" she'd seen in the forest. From there, the characters were jumped by multiple bufonem's and interred in the cell. Later, they were strung up and bled.

All they remember is that the bufonem's master—Maria—told them that their blood would lead the toadfolk to the lost titan, Dhucabra. And Dhucabra would eventually guide all aberrations back into the light.

When the Cords appeared, Maria escaped into the swamp.

Rewards

The *ruby blutvekzelnite* is extremely valuable, even in its weakened state. A buyer who knows what it is may be willing to pay up to 2,000 gp for it. Of course, *ruby blutvekzelnite* turns a lot of heads in Omeria.

There are 20 bits of *vizier's tourmaline* in all. Each bit is worth 50 gp. Like the *blutvekzelnite*, the characters will need to find the right buyer to unload them, as the gems are believed to be exceptionally dangerous in the wrong hands. Ω

TALES OF OMERIA: KALDRFJELL

BY DAVE HAMRICK AND TOM CARTOS

9th-Level Adventure for Fifth Edition

Art by Matias Lazaro, Earl Geier, William McAusland, Maciej Zigorski, and Shutterstock
Cartography by Tom Cartos

Kaldrfjell is a Fifth Edition adventure designed for three to seven players of 8th to 10th level. It is optimized for a party of five characters with an average party level (APL) of 9. Parties with a cleric or paladin as well as those equipped with magic items will have an easier time than those without.

This campaign is set in the DMDave campaign world of Omeria, but you're free to set it anywhere that you like.

Adventure Background

Nestled among the snowy peaks of Kaldrfjell, a northwestern section of the Basilisk's Spine Mountains, sleeps the temple that takes the mountain range's name. It may once have had a title of its own, but if so, it is long forgotten. For centuries it was a place of pilgrimage and sanctuary for many. It was home to an entire monastic school, but now, it is occupied by a lone monk, Elder Maxim. Maxim barred shut the entire lower section of the temple due to neglect as well as a slow incursion of monstrosities from below.

One hundred years ago, when the temple still received pilgrims daily, a horde of barbarian raiders tore through the local townships. The people fled to the temple in hopes of finding safety, but were pursued by the bloodthirsty savages. Most made it inside and the gates were barred. However, this did not deter their attackers who threw themselves against the walls. All hope seemed lost until three heroes appeared from within the temple, their weapons drawn. For four days and four nights, this trio bravely fought off the barbarians until they each finally succumbed to their wounds. Their heroic sacrifice was not in vain. They decimated the horde and the few barbarians who remained fled into the mountains, never to be seen again.

The three heroes were buried within the grounds of the temple, their legendary weapons alongside them, and their names added to the stone tablets that tell the temple's history. No one now remembers exactly where the burial site was, but it is said that if another group of heroes should find themselves in need, they could seek it out and discover new strength there.

Adventure Hooks

The following plot hooks provide some possible ways for the characters to get involved in this adventure.

Find the Tombs of the Heroes. Rumors throughout The Summer Land, the region directly east of Kaldrfjell, point toward the existence of three tombs that hold the bodies of the heroes of Kaldrfjell. Supposedly, each hero wielded a magic weapon of great power. The characters follow the rumors to Kaldrfjell.

Seek Refuge. While traveling through the Kaldrfjell mountain range, the characters find themselves caught in a fierce snowstorm. Nestled in a valley between the peaks the characters discover the temple. As the storm rages, they might dip into the temple's undercroft and discover its secrets.

Clear Out the Vampires. A group of vampires are using Kaldrfjell temple as staging grounds for their attacks on local villages. Clerics in the area have asked the characters to free the region of the vampires' reign of tyranny. If the characters accept, the clerics offer the treasures within as reward for the characters' services.

Kaldrfjell

Kaldrfjell is a snowy mountain temple hidden in the Kaldrfjell Range of the Basilisk's Spine Mountains. Reaching the temple takes two days of travel through circuitous switchbacks blanketed in snow and beset by harsh, freezing winds. The mountain is full of dangerous mountain and arctic creatures such as **blood hawks**, **bulettes**, **orcs**, and **saber-toothed tigers**.

Arrival

When the characters finally reach the temple, read the following:

> Just ahead you see a narrow pass that slips into a snow-covered valley. An ancient wall that once barred entry into the valley now lies in ruin, its gate torn away long ago by villainous barbarians. Tracks in the snow lead up to the collapsed wall, hinting that you may not be the only ones seeking the temple.

The tracks are boot prints made by a gang of bandits who've taken refuge within the main temple. Once the characters reach the wall, read:

> Beyond the ruined wall stands multiple buildings of Khuzhuk architecture. Three pavilions hug the west and south walls of the valley. A massive building sitting atop a 10-foot high landing dominates the east side of the valley.
>
> Although the footprints you saw on the trail visit each of the buildings, most of the footprints lead up the main temple's landing and to its front door.

Temple Grounds

When the characters arrive at the temple, it's snowing. The snow lightly obscures everything and Wisdom (Perception) checks made to hear are made at disadvantage thanks to the wind that howls through the valley.

The temple's landing, stairs, and the other stone surfaces throughout the grounds are covered in slick ice. Noticing the ice requires a DC 10 Wisdom (Perception) check. A creature moving across an icy surface must succeed on a DC 10 Dexterity check or fall prone. A creature moving

through the area at half speed doesn't need to make the save.

The following locations described below are keyed to the map of the temple's grounds on page 68.

1 - Entry

The collapsed gate is the easiest way into the temple. Otherwise, creatures will have to climb along the treacherously steep walls surrounding the grounds.

1a - Gate Ruins. One hundred years ago, a gate stood here, protecting Kaldrfjell from intruders. The barbarians who laid siege to the temple used hill giants to pull away the gate and the arch that supported it. Locals carted away the stone, wood, and iron decades ago.

1b - Ramparts. A broken staircase grants access to anyone who wishes to stand on the entry's old wall. Like most of the stone surfaces of the complex, the stairs and ramparts are slick with ice. If a character fails their Dexterity check to cross the ice by 5 or more, they tumble off the ramparts or stairs, taking 1d6 damage per 10 feet fallen.

2 - Main Grounds

When the characters first reach this section of the temple's grounds, read the following:

> Dozens of boot tracks mar the snow at the center of this broad courtyard. All of the tracks lead up the stairs to the huge temple at the east side of the niche.

The boot prints belonged to a group of bandits who used the temple as temporary reprieve from the winter conditions.

3 - Pavilions

In addition to the main temple, the grounds are occupied by three pavilions in varying stages of ruin.

3a - Passage Below. Partially buried under snow, a stone grate blocks passage to a staircase that descends into the temple's undercroft. Lifting the grate requires a DC 15 Strength check. The stairs are dusted with snow and frozen with ice, making the descent treacherous. The stairs lead to **area 16**a.

3b - Flower Pavilion.

> Snow has crept into this open air pavilion. Interestingly, it appears that the locals still use this area for worship. Dried flowers rest on a pair of stone altars at the west end of the building. Two bronze gongs, encased in ice, dominate the northern wall.

Trap. On the southernmost altar sits a simple wooden and steel chest. Fresh blood, frozen by the cold, coats its edges and the surface of the altar around it. A *detect magic* spell cast on the altar reveals the presence of illusory magic. The chest is unlocked. If a character opens the chest, they discover a golden amulet beset with jewels inside. If a humanoid places their hand into the chest, the creature must make a DC 15 Dexterity saving throw. On a failed saving throw, the creature takes 1d6 slashing damage and their hand is cut off at the wrist. A creature who loses a hand can no longer hold anything with two hands, and can hold only a single object at a time. The *regenerate* spell can restore the lost limb.

Any character who succeeds on a DC 15 Intelligence (Investigation) check recognizes that the amulet and the inside of the chest are illusions. Seeing through the illusion, the character notices that the chest is connected directly to the altar and that the inside of the chest is actually a chute. The trap itself can be disabled with a successful DC 10 Dexterity check using proficiency in thieves' tools.

Treasure. If a character makes a successful DC 15 Intelligence (Investigation) check around the base of the altar, they find a secret compartment. The compartment contains eight severed hands, one of which is relatively fresh. The hands were cut off by the treasure trap. Two of the hands wear gold rings studded with precious gems, valued at 100 gp and 250 gp respectively.

3c - Fubem's Altar. This stone altar is dedicated to the temple's founder, Elder Fubem. Fubem died nearly 300 years ago.

3d - Open Air Pavilion. Unlike the other two pavilions, this pavilion has no walls. Instead, six columns hold up its domed roof. Snow coats the edges of the pavilion and the stone tiles within are slick with ice.

There is nothing of value here.

3e - Temple of Magda the Abolisher.

The front portion of this pavilion is open to the elements. At the center of the temple stands a woman wearing robes, her fists in the air—ready for combat.

The statue represents Magda the Abolisher, one of the temple's greatest teachers of martial arts.

4 - Main Temple

The main temple, commonly referred to as Kaldrfjell, and its landing take up the majority of the snow-covered valley.

4a - Temple Landing. The landing stands 10-feet above the courtyard

and surrounds the temple. Two stone lions rest at the western side of the front landing. The secondary landing lifts the building an additional 6 feet above the courtyard.

A character who succeeds on a DC 15 Intelligence (Investigation) or Wisdom (Survival) check here notices blood on the snow leading to the doors.

4b and 4c - Stairs. The doors at the north and south sides of the building that lead into the temple's undercroft are both barred shut from this side. Removing the bars is easy, but the ice keeps the doors stuck in place. A character must make a successful DC 13 Strength check to break the ice away and open a door. Beyond the doors, stairs descend to **areas 7b** (north) and **7c** (south).

If either door is opened from this side, the ghasts from **area 7a** emerge.

4d - Temple.

The interior of the temple boasts 30-foot high ceilings supported by two rows of three columns each. Four stone benches face a large statue of a smiling man that sits against the easternmost wall.

Characters who discovered the trail of blood outside see that the trail continues into the temple and to the rear stairwell (**area 4e**). The bandits who stayed at the temple were attacked during the night by the vampires that live below. The vampires dragged them into the temple's undercroft.

If the characters make a lot of noise when they enter this area, Elder Maxim enters the temple to see what all the commotion is about.

Statue. A character who succeeds on a DC 15 Intelligence (History or Religion) check recognizes that the statue represents the Khuzhuk god, Qilan, a winter deity. Worship of Qilan ceased a little over one hundred years ago when the monks of Presson's Enclave banned worship of any gods who weren't The Four Generals. It's

believed that Qilan was secretly an aspect of Vapul, a dark god of death and winter. These claims were never substantiated.

4e - Rear Stairwell. Behind the statue of Qilan, a stairway leads down to **area 6**, within the temple's undercroft. The trail of blood from **areas 4a** and **4d** continues down the stairwell.

4f- Shrine to Fubem.

This small room holds a statue of a bald-headed man whose arms are folded in front of him. A simple stone arch rests against the eastern wall.

The shrine is dedicated to Fubem, the temple's founder.

Treasure. The bandits stored their gear here. The characters will find six explorer's packs. Each pack only has half its rations remaining.

4g - Maxim's Cubicle.

This small room contains a small bed, a desk, and a simple stone bench. A wooden chest sits at the foot of the bed.

Encounter: Elder Maxim. Elder Maxim, the temple's caretaker, lives in this room. Unless the characters already encountered him, they find Maxim (NE male human **priest**) working at his desk. Maxim serves the three vampires who live below the temple. Maxim pretends to be a frail old man. He asks the characters to help him with the dangerous creatures who live below the temple. If the characters see through his deception, he drinks a *potion of invisibility* and flees to one of the side doors (**areas 4b** and **4c**).

Treasure. The chest at the foot of Maxim's bed is locked, requiring a DC 15 Dexterity check using proficiency in thieves' tools to unlock. Inside, Maxim keeps gold and silver vestments worth 300 gp. Unless he drank it, Maxim also carries a *potion of invisibility* on his person.

KALDRFJELL
TEMPLE GROUNDS

1A
1B
3A
3B
3C
4B
4F
3D
2
4A
4D
4E
4G
3E
4C

1 Square = 5 Feet

Temple Undercroft

The temple's undercroft is filled with undead whose presence is affected by the vampires that live within. Local villagers know of the temple's nature. They purposely direct adventurers to the temple to sate the vampires' hunger, a fact the characters might discover after (and if) they survive.

The undercroft consists of chambers and corridors that were once a part of the temple's basement and natural caverns created by the creatures who live below the temple. The manmade chambers possess dressed stone walls with 10-foot high ceilings supported by stone pillars. Meanwhile, the caverns' ceilings are much shorter. Unless stated otherwise, a cavern's ceiling is no higher than 7 feet. Although it's cold throughout the entire undercroft, the ice found on the stone surfaces outside are absent here except on the staircase that connects **areas 3a** and **16**.

The following locations described below are keyed to the map of the temple's undercroft on page 69.

6 - Rear Stairwell

The joint staircases behind the statue of Qilan descend 10-feet to a landing, reconnect, and descend an additional 10 feet into a 10-foot corridor.

The door at the west end of the corridor is barred from this side. Removing the bars is easy, but characters who aren't careful might attract the ghasts that stand beyond the door.

7 - Ghast Corridor

The corridor is filled with 6 ravenous **ghasts**. The ghasts wear the robes of the temple's elders. They attack on sight and fight until destroyed.

7a - Barred Door. If the characters approach the door that leads to **area 6** from this side first, the door is barred. Breaking the door open requires a successful DC 20 Strength (Athletics) check.

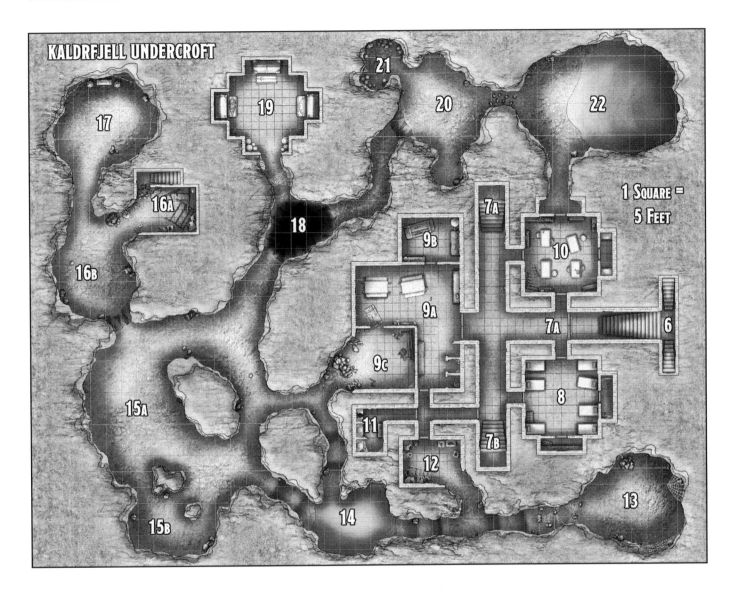

KALDRFJELL UNDERCROFT

1 Square = 5 Feet

7b and 7c - Doors to Outside. The two sets of doors that lead outside are both barred from that side. If the characters did not originally enter through a given set of doors, a character will need to succeed on a DC 20 Strength (Athletics) check to break the doors open. The doors lead to **areas 4b** (north) and **4c** (south).

8 - Priest Quarters

> Seven unmade beds covered in dust fill the room. An old chest rests against the western wall.

There is nothing of value in the room or either of its closets. The rooms appear to have been picked clean by looters.

9 - Commons

The temple's workers prepared meals and ate together here.

9a - Dining Hall.

> Two stone tables flanked by benches crowd the top-half of this old dining room. Everything is covered in cobwebs and dust.

Treasure. A character who searches this area and succeeds on a DC 15 Wisdom (Perception) check finds a platinum signet ring between the cracked tiles. The ring has three circles arranged in a triangle carved into it. The ring is worth 100 gp.

9b - Kitchen.

> This old kitchen hasn't seen use in years.

Encounter: Specters. Three **specters** hide in this small kitchen. They attack immediately and fight until destroyed.

9c - Stores.
This was once where the temple's foodstuffs were stored. Anything of value has long since been removed, eaten, or destroyed.

10 - Study

> Four stone tables beset with stone seats crowd this room. The walls are lined with bookshelves that hold dusty tomes covered in cobwebs.

A skeleton lies on the floor, dead for decades. The skeleton was a human adventurer who entered the temple's undercroft and found himself trapped within; eventually, the zombies cornered him and ate him. The contents of his old pack are unsalvageable.

Treasure. A character who searches the bookshelves finds a small, ornate box covered in dust. Inside the box are three moonstones arranged in a triangular pattern, each one worth 500 gp.

11 - Privy

There is nothing of value in this old restroom.

12 - Storage

> Broken crates and barrels litter the floor of this old room. A gaping hole in the stonework reveals a tunnel that descends into the darkness beyond.

The otyughs that live in the caverns below the temple burst through the storage rooms decades ago. Hunting for food, the creatures destroyed anything of value that the room once held.

The stench of the otyugh cave (**area 13**) can be smelled from this area.

13 - Otyugh Cave

> Mounds of rotten, stiff rodents, dead birds, and other garbage fills this cavern.

Hazard: Stench. A creature who starts their turn in this area must make a DC 10 Constitution saving throw. On a failed saving throw, the creature is poisoned until the start of their next turn. A creature who succeeds on their saving throw is immune to the stench of this cavern for 24 hours.

Encounter: Otyughs. Two **otyughs** sleep under the garbage. The garbage grants both camouflage—the characters won't spot them unless they succeed on a DC 18 Wisdom (Perception) check. As soon as a character comes within reach of the otyughs' tentacles, they attack.

Treasure. Among the otyugh's filth, the characters will find all sorts of treasures. Characters who spend 10 minutes searching through the otyugh's filth will find 100 gp, three golden idols carved to resemble Qilan each worth 250 gp, and a *+1 dagger*.

14 - Stagnant Pool

A 2-foot-deep pool of stagnant water consumes this intersection.

Hazard: Slippery Slides. Climbing out of the pool proves difficult, as the paths that lead into it slope at a 45 degree angle and are covered in slick mud. A creature must succeed on a DC 15 Strength (Athletics) check to pull themselves out of the pool. If the character fails their check by 5 or more, they slide back into the pool and fall prone in the water.

Encounter: Black Puddings. Two **black puddings** wait in the water for creatures to pass through. The oozes are invisible while in the foul water.

15 - Grick Cavern

This large cavern is home to a nest of gricks who lair in its southern end.

15a - Bones.

> The floors of this large cavern are littered with animal bones.

After the gricks kill and eat their prey, they purge the creatures' bones in this chamber. When a creature moves through this room, it must succeed on a DC 10 Dexterity saving throw or step on the bones, causing them to crack. A creature that moves at half speed automatically passes its saving throw.

15b - Grick Lair. Six **gricks** sleep against the walls of this area, camouflaged by the stone. If the characters weren't careful moving through **area 15**a, the gricks are awake and prepared to attack. Otherwise, the creatures remain motionless.

16 - East Entrance

If the characters found the stone grate in **area 3**a and went down the stairs, they can enter the undercroft in this area. The stairs near the top of the steps are slick from the ice (see page 65 for details).

> This room appears to have been a store room. The southwest wall has been destroyed, revealing a dark cavern beyond.

17 - Lost Altar

> This natural cavern is completely empty except for a stone altar resting against the northern wall. Carved into the front of the altar are three circles arranged in a triangular pattern.

Encounter: Wraith and Specters. If a character touches the altar, a **wraith** appears. The wraith looks like one of the temple's elders, but his robes bear the same pattern of circles on the front of the altar. The wraith bellows, "Whom do you serve?" If the characters respond with any name other than "Vapul" it summons four **specters** and attacks.

Treasure. A character who succeeds on a DC 15 Wisdom (Perception) check discovers a secret compartment on the side of the altar. Inside the compartment they find a *wand of the war mage (+2)*.

18 - Pit

> A twenty-foot-wide pit cuts off access to the far side of the corridor.

Hazard: Pit. The pit is 150-feet deep and leads to further sections of The Low (your discretion). It is from within this pit that the creatures that inhabit the temple's undercroft emerge. A narrow ledge connects the western edge of the pit to **area 19**. A character can make a DC 16 Dexterity check. On a success, the character successfully crawls along the ledge. If the character fails the check, they make no progress. And if the character fails the check by 5 or more, they fall into the pit, taking 1d6 damage for every 10 feet they fall (15d6 in all).

Hazard: Bats. Bats line the sides of the pit's walls. The bats can be spotted with a successful DC 15 Wisdom (Perception) check. If the characters make too much noise, the bats stir and erupt from the pit.

Any character standing within 5 feet of the pit must make a DC 10 Dexterity saving throw to avoid falling into the pit. A character climbing along the ledge of the pit makes this check at disadvantage. Other than the danger the bats present characters who are near the pit's edge, the bats are harmless.

19 - The Tomb of the Three

> Three stone sarcophagi rest against the walls of this small chamber. Each sarcophagus is decorated with an ornate object: the westernmost sarcophagus bears a large, bronze tower shield; the northernmost sarcophagus features a glimmering longsword; and the easternmost sarcophagus presents a silver longbow.

This is the final resting place of the three "heroes" who repelled the barbarian forces from the temple thirty years ago. However, the story was a sham. The heroes were actually vampires and the barbarians were slayers who came to rid the mountain of their presence. When the characters try to take the vampires' weapons, the vampires emerge from the sarcophagi and attack. Treat each as a **vampire spawn**.

The three weapons are fakes, used to lure adventurers to the vampires' lair where they attempt to trap the adventurers within the pit. Each one is a mundane item painted to look as if it possesses magical properties. A *detect magic* spell sees through the ruse, as does a successful DC 13 Intelligence (Investigation) check made on an item.

20 - Cavern

The body of one of the missing bandits lies in this cavern, her blood drained.

21 - Mushroom Cavern

> This small cavern is filled with fluffy, green mushrooms.

There is nothing of value here.

22 - Dark Pool

> A pool of black, still water dominates the eastern end of this natural cavern.

The pool is 5 feet deep at its deepest part.

Treasure. The remains of a dead dwarven adventurer lie at the bottom of the pool. The dwarf wore a helmet that it believed to be a *helmet of water breathing. Identify* spells cast on the helmet offer similar misleading information. The helmet is actually cursed. Any creature wearing the helmet when the helmet enters water immediately falls unconscious, as per the *sleep* spell. Ω

TALES OF OMERIA: DROWN

BY DAVE HAMRICK

11th-Level Adventure for Fifth Edition

Art by Matias Lazaro, William McAusland and Rick Hershey
Cartography by Dave Hamrick

This side trek is designed for three to seven 11th to 16th level characters and is optimized for five characters with an average party level (APL) of 11.

Likely, the characters will have tracked the vampire to its lair after following clues that point to its existence.

Adventure Background

An often overlooked feature of vampires is their ability to exist in environments that do not require air. As such, some crafty vampires move their lairs to underwater caverns. These remote locations offer vampires several advantages such as a lack of air for creatures who'd hunt it and an overall absence of sunlight. Because of the vampire's weakness against running water, these submerged lairs must be at the bottom of dismal swamps or murky lakes.

Adventure Hooks

If you don't already have a hook in mind, roll a d10 and refer to the Aquatic Vampire Adventure Hooks table, or choose a hook that best fits your current campaign.

The Aquatic Vampire

Both the **aquatic vampire** and its **vampire spawn** have a swim speed of 30 ft.

For its Shapechanger feature, the aquatic vampire can change into a quipper. While in this form, it can't speak, and it has a walking speed of 0 ft. but it gains a swim speed of 40 ft. Its statistics, other than its size and speed, are unchanged.

Anything it is wearing transforms with it, but nothing it is carrying does. It reverts to its true form if it dies. It can use its bite in its quipper form.

Also, instead of transforming into mist, the vampire can become a cloud of sentient blood. This blood form works the same as its mist form, except it has a swim speed of 40 ft.

Aquatic Vampire Adventure Hooks.

d10	Adventure Hook
1	Entire fields of crops wither and die in the area surrounding the haunted pond.
2	Foul undead have been attacking passersby traveling on a popular road that cuts through a swamp.
3	A noble's daughter disappeared near the lake. Villagers believe that it is the work of a vampire who appears every twenty years.
4	The headless remains of bodies are found floating in the nearby swamp. Local medical examiners believe that it might be the work of an undead creature covering its tracks.
5	Two children return to a village claiming that they saw evil faces in the water of an old pond.
6	The vampire came into a village demanding a sacrifice of six children by the full moon. It threatens to kill everyone in the village unless this tribute is paid.
7	The vampire seeks revenge against the local priest who, in his/her younger days, eradicated the vampire's old nest.
8	While parked next to a murky pond, an armed wagon loaded with treasure, relief funds for the war, is torn apart. All of the guards are killed except for one who claims that horrible creatures rose from the water and drank the blood of the victims.
9	One of the characters dreams of the aquatic vampire and its lair.
10	The fiancé of one of the character's allies has been turned into a vampire spawn. To save him/her, the characters must track the vampire who turned him/her.

instead of a flying speed. And if water can pass through a space, the blood can do so without squeezing; unlike its mist form, the blood can pass through water.

For its Children of the Night feature, the aquatic vampire can choose to call 2d4 **swarms of quippers** as well as bats or rats, or 2d4 **reef sharks**.

The Vampire's Lair

The region surrounding the aquatic vampire's cave is warped by the creature's unnatural presence, creating any of the following effects:

• There's a noticeable increase in the population of quippers and sharks in the region. Aquatic plants within 500 feet of the lair become black and tangled and sometimes look like outstretched claws.

• The surfaces of water within 500 feet of the lair reflect perversions of the original image, making living creatures seem gaunt or undead.

• A creeping fog clings to the surface of the water within 500 feet of the vampire's lair. The fog occasionally takes eerie forms, such as grasping claws and writhing serpents.

• The entirety of the vampire's lair is considered desecrated. All undead creatures in the aquatic vampire's lair have advantage on saving throws.

If the aquatic vampire is destroyed, these effects end after 2d6 days.

Area Description

Unless otherwise stated, the aquatic vampire's lair has the following features.

Dimensions & Terrain. The lair has short ceilings throughout, with tunnels and passages no higher than they are wide. The walls are made of solid rock. Most of the floors are made of rock, too, except areas where silt has collected.

Underwater. All areas of the aquatic vampire's lair are completely submerged except for the pocket of air in **area 5**. Refer to the rules on characters holding their breath (Chapter 8) and underwater combat (Chapter 9) in the *PHB* as well as the rules for underwater environments in Chapter 5 of the *DMG*.

Light. There is no light within the vampire's underwater lair.

Sound. Not only is it difficult to see in the aquatic vampire's lair, but it's hard to hear as well. A creature without a swim speed has disadvantage on Wisdom (Perception) checks that rely on hearing while underwater.

Visibility. The vampire's fiendish presence turns the water cloudy. The vampire, its spawn, and the vampire's minions can see through the water as if it was clear, up to 60 ft. However, all other creatures can only see up to 10 ft in front of themselves.

1 - Entrance

The entrance into the aquatic vampire's lair is a steep descent from the hole at the bottom of the lake, lagoon, or other pool of water in which the lair is found. The narrow tunnel is no more than 10 feet between the floor and the ceiling.

Trap. The walls, ceiling, and floors of the entrance are covered in thick, black seaweed. On initiative count 10 (losing initiative ties) the seaweed makes an attack against each creature within this area with a +9 to hit. A creature hit by the seaweed takes 10 (3d6) bludgeoning damage and is restrained. A creature that starts its turn in the area and is already restrained by the seaweed takes 10 (3d6) bludgeoning damage. A creature restrained by the seaweed can use

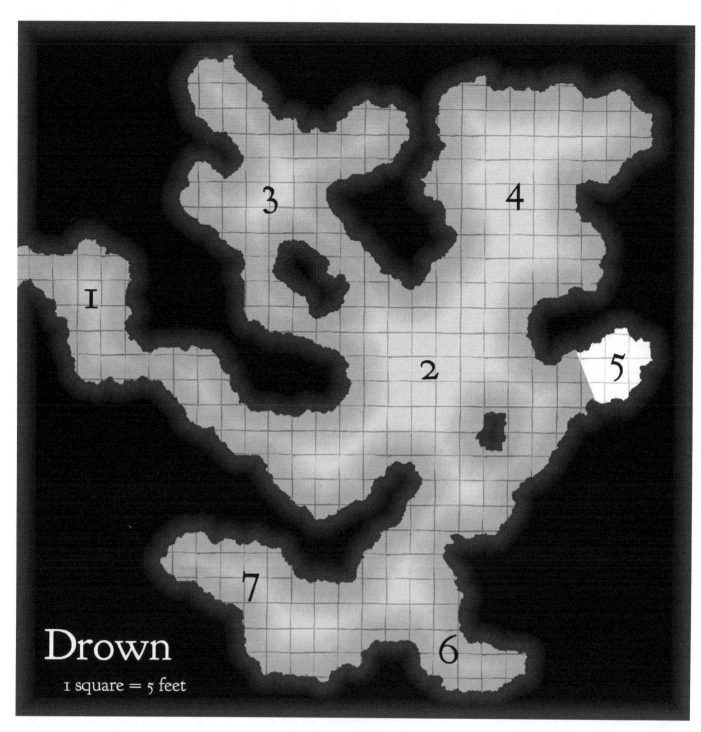

Drown

1 square = 5 feet

its action to make a DC 17 Strength or Dexterity check (the creature's choice), freeing itself on a success. A creature can also make an attack against the seaweed to free itself. A 5 x 5 patch of seaweed has AC 13, 3 hp, and is immune to psychic damage and resistant to bludgeoning and piercing damage. A destroyed patch of seaweed reforms on initiative count 20.

The seaweed withers away after the aquatic vampire is killed.

2 - Guardian
This large, open area has 30-foot high ceilings.

Creature Description. A **rusted iron golem** stands here looking for intruders. The rusted iron golem has the same statistics as an **iron golem** except with the following changes:
- Its movement speed is 20 ft.
- Its Dexterity score is 5 (-3).
- In addition to its other immunities,

the golem is immune to lightning damage.

- Instead of Fire Absorption, the golem has Lightning Absorption (as the flesh golem).

- **New Trait: Rust.** Any nonmagical weapon made of metal that hits the golem corrodes. After dealing damage, the weapon takes a permanent and cumulative -1 penalty to damage rolls. If its penalty drops to -5 the weapon is destroyed. Nonmagical ammunition made of metal that hits the golem is destroyed after dealing damage.

- If the golem hits a creature wearing metal armor or carrying a metal shield with its Slam attack, the armor or shield (creature's choice if it has both equipped) takes a permanent and cumulative -1 penalty to the AC it offers. Armor reduced to an AC of 10 or a shield that drops to a +0 bonus is destroyed.

The iron golem attacks intruders relentlessly until it is told otherwise by the aquatic vampire or one of its spawn.

3 - Cave of Spawn

The aquatic vampire's spawn rest in this portion of the cavern.

Creature Information. There are four **vampire spawn** who rest in this cavern.

Tactics. The vampire spawn enjoy feigning innocence to lure unsuspecting prey. They leave one or more of their kindred at the center of the cavern in plain view, usually the one among them most recently turned. It may even be wearing rusted manacles. While the creature weeps and begs to be saved, the others use the murky water, their spider climb, and their Stealth to get the drop on the others. The vampires employ hit-and-run tactics: they attack, grapple, pull the creature into the murk, and drink its blood. Understanding that most creatures can't see more than 10 ft. into the water, they try to divide and conquer whenever possible.

4 - Treasure Vault

The aquatic vampire keeps its ill-gotten gains in the northernmost section of its lair.

Treasure. The aquatic vampire's treasure hoard includes 123,000 cp, 29,700 sp, 9,500 GP, and 2,100 pp. There are also 120 gems worth an average of 10 gp each, and a golden scepter worth 1,000 gp (see below). Although there are a few rusted chests available to carry away the treasure, for the most part, it is strewn about the cavern floor and should take hours to collect.

Trap. There is a golden scepter sitting upon the pile of treasure in the cavern. Removing the scepter triggers a controlled collapse of the ceiling. Each creature in the cavern when the ceiling collapses must make a DC 15 Dexterity saving throw. A creature that fails on its saving throw takes 35 (10d6) bludgeoning damage and is pinned under the collapsed rock. While pinned, the creature is restrained and takes 7 (2d6) bludgeoning damage at the start of each of its turns.

A creature can use its action to free the pinned target (including the target itself) with a successful DC 18 Strength (Athletics) check.

On a successful saving throw, a creature takes half as much damage and isn't restrained. However, its passage out of this area might be permanently blocked. Plus, all of the treasure is buried under the rubble and cannot be easily recovered.

Spotting the trap requires a DC 15 Wisdom (Perception) check. A character with proficiency in thieves' tools can disarm the check with a successful DC 15 Dexterity or Intelligence check (character's choice).

5 - Air Pocket

The vampire keeps its prisoners in this air pocket. There is a 50% chance that the vampire's next victim (a **commoner**) is here. The commoner has one level of exhaustion and is frightened of all vampires.

6 - False Coffin

A rusted iron coffin dominates the center of this cavern.

Antipathy. The front of the cavern is enchanted with the *antipathy/sympathy* spell (DC 17) with the antipathy feature targeting humanoids. The spell is intended to make intruders believe the coffin has more value than it actually does.

Coffin Trap. The iron lid is easily removed by any creature with a Strength score of 15 or better. The inside of the coffin is magically darkened and cannot be seen into, not even with a trait like a warlock's Devil's Sight. A creature that reaches inside the coffin immediately finds itself grappled (escape DC 17). On initiative count 10 (losing initiative ties), a creature grappled by the coffin takes 9 (2d8) necrotic damage and its hit point maximum is reduced by an amount equal to the necrotic damage taken. If the creature's hit point maximum is reduced by 1/4th of its hit point total, its arm completely withers to nothing and the grapple ends.

A creature without its arm can no longer hold anything with two hands, and it can only hold a single object a time. A *regenerate* spell restores both the lost appendage and its hit point maximum.

Recognizing the trap for what it is requires a successful DC 17 Intelligence (Arcana) check. A *dispel magic* spell cast against a 5th-level spell disables the hungering darkness within the coffin for 10 minutes. Once the darkness is removed, there is nothing else in the coffin.

7 - The Vampire's True Cavern

The vampire's true resting place is in the empty cavern to the south.

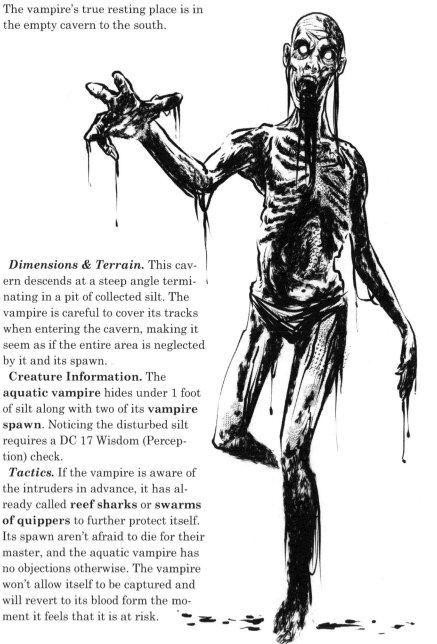

Dimensions & Terrain. This cavern descends at a steep angle terminating in a pit of collected silt. The vampire is careful to cover its tracks when entering the cavern, making it seem as if the entire area is neglected by it and its spawn.

Creature Information. The **aquatic vampire** hides under 1 foot of silt along with two of its **vampire spawn**. Noticing the disturbed silt requires a DC 17 Wisdom (Perception) check.

Tactics. If the vampire is aware of the intruders in advance, it has already called **reef sharks** or **swarms of quippers** to further protect itself. Its spawn aren't afraid to die for their master, and the aquatic vampire has no objections otherwise. The vampire won't allow itself to be captured and will revert to its blood form the moment it feels that it is at risk.

Concluding the Adventure: Horror in the Water

If the aquatic vampire's lair is disrupted, it will flee to find a new lair. The new lair may be in another body of water or it might even be above ground. While it will want vengeance against those that harmed it and its children, ultimately, it will turn its attention back to its dark goals. Thus, it is up to the characters to seek the vampire and trap it once more. Ω

APPENDICES

APPENDIX A
CYCLOPÆDIA OMERIA

BY DAVE HAMRICK
ART BY ANDREW KRAHNKE, RICK HERSHEY, WILLIAM MCAUSLAND, AND MACIEJ ZAGORSKI
CARTOGRAPHY BY DARRYL T. JONES, DAVE HAMRICK, DYSON LOGOS, AND TOM CARTOS

The Village of Grihoo

The tree line breaks, exposing a small village consisting of squat, expertly-built stone buildings, 14 in all. The buildings are built of sandstone bricks. The majority of the buildings flank a narrow canal leading from the edge of the forest to the temple at the far northern end of the village.

The temple measures roughly 70 feet by 70 feet and stands 50 feet tall. The exterior walls are carved to look like hundreds of snakes crawling over top of each other. Two female human warriors wearing elaborate headdresses stand guard at the temple's entrance. Joining them are five muscular, 12-foot tall apes wearing bronze armor who climb over the sides of the building.

At either side of the temple are two 200-foot tall obelisks made of steel. Roughly 10 feet from the top of each of these pylons there is a small window from which green light glows.

Plenty of sunlight illuminates the village during the day. And at night, the village is lit with torches. The pylons emit a dull green glow as well.

The village is home to over 30 Serpent Whisperers of Grihoo. The warrior women keep goats, chickens, and other livestock in the area. There are also needleblast boas that freely roam the village, offering additional protection where needed.

How to Use This Resource

Grihoo Village can be used as part of any campaign that takes place in a jungle, deserted island, or anywhere else a small Aztec- or Mayan-inspired village would be appropriate. The default descriptions included in this document are specifically for The Serpent Whisperers of Grihoo, an amazon warrior tribe featured in the adventure series *Titan's Heir*. However, rules for making your own custom village are included as well.

History

Approximately 500 years ago, the *Panaakebaag*, a danaavrakti slave ship sailing from the island of Elsath, was caught in a ferocious storm. Unable to successfully navigate the waters, the spellcasters onboard the ship evacuated with teleportation magic, leaving all 101 slave women in its cargo to perish. Whether it was the will of Suen or simply good luck, the ship instead ran aground near a small group of islands in the Ocean of Warna.

Nearly half their ranks died that first hard year on the island. But those who did survive hardened themselves to this new reality. And even though the island was a cruel mother, it granted the women something they'd never had before: freedom.

Eventually, the women discovered that they weren't the only ones on the island. At the southern end of the island stood a mysterious temple carved to look like hundreds of snakes crawling over top of each other. Fearing the temple, the women stayed away. But eventually, a strange creature came out. The creature looked nothing like them. It had more arms, more legs, and its head was misshapen and alien. But it spoke in a soft, soothing voice they could feel at the back of their minds and promised the women that it would only help them. The creature gave the women food. It helped them build a village around its temple. In time, it also gave them men with whom they could propagate their kind. In return, it asked that they never allow another living creature to enter the temple which it called Grihoo.

As the years passed, the women—or phusaphusaana as the strange creature dubbed them—forgot their origins and knew only the temple and its serpents.

Serpent Whisperers of Note

When the Ivorian Guild first discovered the phusaphusaana in the middle of the Ocean of Warna, they dubbed them "Amazon warriors. " This name came from the popular legend of the all-female warrior tribes who hailed from the mythical Jungles of Amazonia. Since then, the term has stuck. Armed with thick, obsidian-lined clubs, these warriors of Grihoo race through the dense jungles of the Skeleton Key, eager to combat any who should seek to uncover the secrets of their island protectorate.

Important Serpent Whisperers include the following NPCs. See Appendix D for statistics.

- **Viothye** is the village elder and leader of the Serpent Whisperers. She is a LN **amazon warrior** with 55 hp.
- **Ykyope** is the village's greatest warrior and tracker. She is a LN **amazon warrior** with 55 hp.
- **Vuda** is Ykyope's sister and a tracker for the Serpent Whisperers. She is joined by two **tigers** named Ekda and Xotnoe. She is a CN **amazon warrior**.
- **Toumida** (is the village's barter arbiter. No major trades happen unless she grants permission. She is a LG **amazon warrior**.
- **Dexece** is the head of security for the temple and the leader of the Serpent Guard. She is a LN **serpent guard**.
- **Motewno** is the alpha of the **Heirs of Kong**. Often, he is found scouting the outside of the village.

Serpent Whisperer Names. If you need a quick name for a Serpent Whisperer, choose an option or roll for a result on the Serpent Whisperer Names table below.

Serpent Whisperers Names.

d12	Name
1	Alliesia
2	Beiitane
3	Blumyope
4	Eiyne
5	Kedgone
6	Moktane
7	Nyestra
8	Phodora
9	Pouthysose
10	Thulasca
11	Uyadia
12	Valiliope

The Hunters

The Serpent Whisperers who leave the village to hunt for creatures in the forest and scout for other dangers to the island are collectively known as "the hunters." Ykyope is the leader of the hunters. Ykyope's sister, Vuda, is also a hunter and considered by many to be the village's best tracker.

The Serpent Guard

The temple is protected by the legendary Serpent Guard, the fiercest warriors among the Serpent Whisperers. Each member of the Serpent Guard wields the powerful tepoztopilli, a polearm topped with a broad wooden head capable of crushing enemy spines with a single blow. The tepoztopilli gives the serpent guards the advantage of reach while allowing them to use their massive tower shields for added defense. There are six total Serpent Guards who live and operate in the village.

The Heirs of Kong

The magic that courses through the veins of The Skeleton Key has had a strange effect on the flora and fauna indigenous to the island. Animals grow larger and are generally more intelligent. Plus, they seemingly possess a greater sense of self. Case in point: the Heirs of Kong. These 12-foot-tall apes inhabit the jungles and forests of the key. And until the Serpent Whisperers of Grihoo arrived, the heirs were the dominant guardians of the island.

Intelligent and psionically active, the heirs do not consider themselves servants of the Serpent Whisperers, rather joint custodians of the island. The heirs even have their own community separate from the Serpent Whisperers. In this community, they decide on matters important to both the island and the heirs. Regardless, when the island is challenged, they almost always join forces with the Amazons. Individually, the apes and the warrior women are powerful. But together, they are an unstoppable force of nature.

The original Kong was rumored to be a 30-foot tall ape that lived in the nameless mountain range at the center of the island. However, no proof has emerged that such a creature ever existed. Regardless, the apes still happily carry the moniker.

There are ten Heirs of Kong who operate in and around the village.

Locations in the Village

Refer to the map overleaf for the following locations in the village.

A - Canal

A stone canal runs the length of the village. The water pours magically from the Temple of Grihoo 300-feet north of the village. No matter the season, the water is cool and refreshing. The canals are two feet deep and able to support all of the villager's canoes.

B - Serpent Whisperer Home

The majority of the Serpent Whisperers live in sandstone buildings built along the canal that runs through the center of the village.

Area Description. While the layouts may vary, Serpent Whisperer homes have the following features:

Dimensions & Terrain. All of the buildings have 10-foot high ceilings. The floors are paved with stone tiles. Because the "creature of the temple" (see the section on History) taught the early Serpent Whisperers architecture, the buildings are expertly-constructed. Most of the buildings are built onto a foundation that lifts them from the ground to protect the interiors from flooding. Hand-woven rugs are common throughout the village.

Doors. The doors are built from solid wood. Although the doors can be barred from the inside, everyone in the village leaves their doors open, including Viothye.

Beds. The Serpent Whisperers sleep in linen hammocks or on cots covered in animal furs. On the map of the Grihoo village, the number of beds present in the building is usually the number of inhabitants that live in a given building.

Roof Access. Many of the Serpent Whisperers' homes have staircases that grant access to the rooves of the buildings.

Supplies. All Serpent Whisperer homes contain 1d4 + 1 days worth of food and water per inhabitant.

Treasure. Consummate barterers, the Serpent Whisperers have no need for currency. However, a few have collected trinkets, gems, and other items of interest. There is a 50% chance that a character who succeeds on a DC 13 Intelligence (Investigation) check finds a treasure stash in each building. Roll 1d4 times on the Serpent Whisperer Treasure table below to determine what the character finds. Refer to Chapter 7 of the DMG for gems, art objects, and magic item tables.

GRIHOO VILLAGE

1 square = 5 feet

patreon.com/tomcartos

Serpent Whisperer Treasure.

d20	Treasure
1-15	A random trinket
16	A gemstone worth 10 gp
17	2d4 cp
18	An art object worth 25 gp
19	A random martial weapon (GM's descretion).
20	A magic item from Magic Item Table A

C - Bartering Center

All major trade is to be performed at the bartering center. There, Toumida presides with her young daughter Pheice (non-combatant **commoner**). The Serpent Whisperers aren't interested in gold. Instead, they value trade.

The Bartering Center trade table gives a list of common items traded for in the Bartering Center as well as the "trade values" for the items. For example, a character who wishes to trade for a spear which has a trade value of 2 must trade another item with a trade value of 2 such as two days worth of rations. See Appendix A for common trade values.

For items that aren't listed on the trade table, a character can attempt to persuade Toumida or another barterer of the item's value. Have the character make a DC 10 Charisma (Persuasion) check. On a failed check, the item is worthless. On a successful check, the item has a trade value of 1d4.

D - Fishing Supplies

The large hut at the eastern end of the village contains a stockpile of fishing supplies. Many of the women who live in the village who do not fill the roles of hunters or guards act as gatherers and fishers.

E - Food Stores

In the winter and during times of drought, Toumida keeps a stockpile of

TEMPLE OF GRIHOO

preserved foodstuffs and water so the village perseveres.

There are enough food and water supplies in this area to keep all of the Serpent Whisperers fed and hydrated for 1 month. The door to this area is kept locked. All three council members have a key to the stores. Breaking down a door requires a DC 15 Strength (Athletics) check or a successful DC 15 Dexterity check using proficiency in thieves' tools.

F - Serpent Statue

At the center of the village is a serpent statue carved to look like a head of Grihoo. Viothye gives announcements from this area. Also, when lashes are given out as punishment, the lashes are performed at the statue (see Law and Order).

G - Elder's Hall

Although Viothye, Toumida, and Dexece make up the ruling body of the Serpent Whisperers, the council permits the other adults of the village to meet to discuss important matters democratically.

H - Armory

The armory consists not only of Serpent Whisperer weapons (see *Trade Goods*), but weapons collected from outsiders to the island, including polearms, swords, maces, morningstars, and rapiers. There are also two suits of leather armor and six shields of varying makes. The door to this area is kept locked. All three council members have a key to the armory. Breaking down a door requires a DC 15 Strength (Athletics) check or a successful DC 15 Dexterity check using proficiency in thieves' tools.

I - Training Room

The hunters and trackers of the Serpent Whisperers utilize their fighting skills every day in the forests surrounding the village. However, the Serpent Guard's members rarely leave the village. Thus, this use this area to improve their fighting skills.

Here, they can spar, exercise, and practice archery.

J - Tower

A 35-foot-high tower overlooks the village. At all times, there is one member of the Serpent Guard who keeps watch. The tower is also one of the sturdiest buildings in the entire village. During times of flooding or severe storms, it can be used as a shelter. The base of the tower contains dried foodstuffs and water.

K - Village Elder's Home

Viothye lives at the northside of town in a simple stone building. She is joined by her lover, Cleothye (KLEE-oh-thyay). Her home is the same as the ones described in area B.

L - Hunters Circle

Ykyope and the other hunters live in thatch and mud huts at the northwestern edge of the village. They consider themselves "creatures of the forest" and prefer the rugged setting. Late nights, the hunters sit around the fire, roasting the day's hunt. Vuda's two tigers sleep by the fire, guarding the hunters.

Serpent Pipe. While the hunters celebrate the rewards of their hunt, they pass a wooden pipe carved in the likeness of a serpent to one another. The pipe contains dried and ground ubaco root, a hallucinogenic drug. A creature who smokes from the pipe must make a DC 10 Constitution saving throw. On a failed saving throw, the creature is poisoned for 10 minutes.

M - Hunter Hut

The five huts at the northwestern edge of the camp are homes to the hunters.

Area Description. Each of the hunter's huts (Ykyope's included) have the following features:

Dimensions & Terrain. All of the huts are round, doorless, bamboo and mud huts with seven-foot-high thatch ceilings. The floors are bare earth. Be-

cause this end of the village is slightly higher than the lower portion, the effects of flooding aren't as severe here. When the flooding does get bad, however, the hunters retreat further into the forest or into the tower (area J).

Beds. The Serpent Whisperers sleep on cots covered in animal furs. On the map of the Grihoo village, the number of beds present in a hunt is usually the number of inhabitants that live in a given building.

Supplies. All of the hunters' huts contain 1d4 + 1 days worth of food and water per inhabitant.

Treasure. There is a 50% chance that a character who succeeds on a DC 13 Intelligence (Investigation) check finds a treasure stash in each hut. Use the Serpent Whisperer treasure table in **area B** to determine what the character finds.

N - Ykyope's Hut

Ykyope, leader of the hunters, lives in the largest hut with her sister, Vuda. The hut has the same features described in **area M**.

O - The Serpents' Path

The path and canals lead 300-feet north to the Temple of Grihoo. See the adventure module Grihoo for details.

Side Quests

There are plenty of tasks that Viothye and other members of the Serpent Whisperers need doing in and around the village. Not only will these tasks help the character earn trust with the Serpent Whisperers (see *Earning Trust* in the **Grihoo** adventure module), but it may lead to unexpected rewards and discoveries.

Introduce as many or as few of these side quests as you like. Suggestions for NPCs who trigger them are in the description, but if a different NPC fits your story better, feel free to change it. If you can't decide which side quest to choose, roll a d8.

Creatures that appear in **bold** type refer to monsters stat blocks that appear in either the *MM* or Appendix D. See the ***Grihoo*** adventure in this book for details.

1. **Collect Zujadilla for Toumida.** Toumida, the village's trade arbiter, is running low on zujadilla (zoo-ha-dee-ya), a strange, yellow-and-purple striped fruit that grows on the southern end of the island. To find the zujadilla, the characters must spend a day exploring the hexes south of the village. Have each character who participated make a DC 10 Wisdom (Survival) check. On a successful check, roll 1d6 + the character's Wisdom modifier to determine how many zujadillas the character finds. For each zujadilla found, the characters add that amount to their next Earning Trust check (maximum of +10). This task is only available once per month.

2. **Hunt with Ykyope.** Ykyope asks the characters to join her on a hunt for a creature that poses a major threat to the village: a **tyrannosaurus rex**. If the characters agree, the characters are joined by Ykyope (LN **amazon warrior** with 55 hp) and six **amazon warriors**. After a day of hunting, the characters and Ykyope eventually track the beast to its lair. The tyrannosaurus is aggressive and cruel, and will attack a creature until it is truly and totally dead. If the characters succeed on this mission with Ykyope, they add +5 to their next Earning Trust check.

3. **Retrieve Viothye's Key.** In the night, Vuda stole Viothye's key to the temple (see ***Grihoo***) from around her neck and vanished into the forest. Viothye asks the characters to track down Vuda and return the key. However, she does not wish Vuda to be killed. The Serpent Whisperers will handle the punishment of Vuda. Vuda (CN **amazon warrior**) and her two tigers can be found in a cave 20 miles north of the village. Vuda suffers from a condition known as *firemind* which makes her act paranoid and irrational. When the characters find her, she's babbling incoherently. If the characters subdue Vuda and return the key to Viothye, they get a +20 bonus to their next Earning Trust check. However, if they kill Vuda or fail to return the key, they get a -10 penalty to their next Earning Trust check.

4. **Find the Monster Men Camp.** Viothye asks the characters to help her find a dangerous group of creatures who live north of the nameless mountains. She refers to them as "monster men" and warns the characters that they are cruel cannibals and killers. The Monster Men's camp is detailed further in the Island Exploration section. When the characters enter the hex with the Monster Man camp, a successful DC 15 Wisdom (Survival) check reveals the path back to the camp itself. Once the characters find the camp and report its location back to Viothye, they earn +10 to their next Earning Trust check.

5. **Rescue Pheice.** Toumida's daughter, Pheice (FEE-shay) has vanished into the forest. Toumida suspects that Pheice was out picking zujadilla and isn't particularly worried. If one or more characters spend an hour searching the forest, they find Pheice in an empty clearing surrounded by holes in the ground (see the *Grihoo Holes* location in the Island Exploration section for details). She's sitting on a rock, frightened. The Heads of Grihoo are trying to eat Pheice. When the characters try to save her, 1d6 + 1 **Heads of Grihoo** attack. If one or more of the heads is destroyed, all of the heads retract back into their holes. Once Toumida learns that the characters saved her daughter, the characters earn +15 on their next Earning Trust check.

6. **Find Boy and Man.** Viothye approaches the characters and asks them to track a pair of men who escaped the temple and fled into the forest. She will not explain why the men were in the temple or why they are important but promises that if the characters can find them—alive or dead—they will earn the trust of herself and the other Serpent Whisperers. Man and Boy can be found in the abandoned mine on the western edge of the nameless mountain range. See ***The Skeleton Key*** adventure module or the *Man and Boy* Addendum in ***Grihoo*** for details. If the characters find the two, they earn a +20 bonus on their next Earning Trust check.

7. **Kill Xeopesia.** In a series of ruins at the north end of the island, a dangerous **medusa** named Xeopesia (ZEE-oh-PAY-sha) hides from the amazon warriors. Xeopesia also knows many of the island's secrets—she may even use her knowledge as a bargaining tool. Xeopesia's lair is detailed in the Island Exploration section. If the characters find and kill Xeopesia, they gain a +10 bonus to their next Earning Trust check.

8. **The Chamber of Titans.** Vuda, during one of her manic episodes, begrudgingly approaches the characters with a request: tell her what is on the wall of the Chamber of Titans. In return, she will give the characters "a great treasure." She explains that the chamber is in the temple, first corridor on the right, first room on the left. If they can return with a description of what they saw, they discover that she has no rewards to give them. In fact, she doesn't even remember asking them to perform the task and curses at them for suggesting such. Moreover, if the characters are caught by the Serpent Whisperers, they will need to prove their innocence to the other Serpent Whisperers (see *Law and Order* below).

Law and Order

The Serpent Whisperers adhere to a strict set of rules that they all mostly know and follow. Anyone who violates the rules must prove their innocence before a council of three: Viothye, Toumida, and Dexece.

Their laws are as follows, listed from least severe to most severe. The right column has penalties or modifiers added to a violator's ability checks when making Proving Innocence rolls.

Enforcement

Dexece and the Serpent Guard maintains order in the village. If the violator is particularly dangerous, they employ the help of the Heirs of Kong. The Serpent Guard only wishes to apprehend the violator but will kill them in order to protect the village.

Proving Innocence

Someone charged with a crime must argue their case before Viothye, Toumida, and Dexece. The creature has one hour to make their case. At the end of the hour, have the creature make three Charisma (Deception or Persuasion) checks. The DCs for each of the checks are determined using the council DCs check table below. Certain laws are less severe than others; add or subtract the modifiers shown on the Serpent Whisperers' laws table to the requisite Charisma checks. After the checks are made, consult the Proving Innocence table to see how the character did.

Note: All of the laws strictly apply to Serpent Whisperers. For example: While no creature may kill a Serpent Whisperer, the Serpent Whisperers are free to kill other creatures, and so forth. They do not care (or understand) the hypocrisy inherent in their one-sided laws.

Punishments

There are two types of punishments granted by the Serpent Whisperers: severe and minor. A humanoid found guilty and given a punishment may

Serpent Whisperer Laws.

Law	Modifier
No one shall own a Serpent Whisperer as property.	-5
No one shall kill a Serpent Whisperer.	-5
None shall enter the temple except for the village elder (Viothye) and the head of security (Dexece).	-5
All Serpent Whisperers are equal and must treat each other as equals. Furthermore, non-Serpent Whisperers must treat all Serpent Whisperers as their superior.	+0
All Serpent Whisperers must do their part to help the community.	+5
All Serpent Whisperers are required to bear a minimum of two children. Daughters remain in the village and sons are given to the sea at the Cliff of Eyes (see the Island Exploration section).	+0
No one shall steal from a Serpent Whisperer.	+0
No one shall lie to a Serpent Whisperer.	+10

Council DCs.

Council Member	DC
Dexece	18
Toumida	10
Viothye	13

Proving Innocence.

Result	Outcome
0 successes	The violator is given a severe punishment.
1 success	The violator is given a minor punishment.
2 successes	The violator is found not guilty. The next time they commit a crime, their Proving Innocence checks are made with disadvantage.
3 successes	The violator is found not guilty with no further consequences.

choose the actual punishment given. The punishments are as follows:

Severe Punishments. The worst punishments that the Serpent Whisperers offer are as follows:

Death. The violator is beheaded before the temple's steps. Their body is given to the Heirs of Kong to tear apart.

Exile. The violator is exiled from the village and cannot come within

3 miles or suffer the pain of death at the hands of the Serpent Guard. Furthermore, the violator is given a brand on their forehead to remind those of his/her crimes. A creature with the brand has disadvantage on Charisma (Persuasion) checks when dealing with creatures who understand the meaning of the brand. Magical healing of 6th level or higher, such as *heal* and *regenerate*, removes the brand.

Minor Punishments. Those whose crimes are not as severe suffer the following punishments at the hands of the Serpent Whisperers:

The Hole. The creature is placed into a six-foot-deep muddy hole in the ground. The top of the hole is covered by a 6-inch-thick cylindrical stone, with 1-inch wide holes dug into it. Removing the stone requires one or more creatures with a combined Strength scores of 15 to move it. The creature must remain in the hole for 2d6 days. They are given no food or water while in the hole. If the creature escapes the hole before its time is served, the Serpent Whisperers add an additional 4d6 days to the time that the creature must spend in the hole. If another creature is found giving the creature food or water or assisting the creature in escape, that

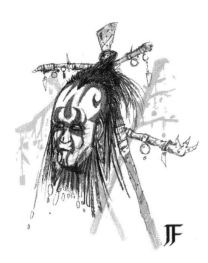

creature is charged by the council as if it had committed the same exact crime as the creature in the hole, no matter how severe. If a creature dies from starvation or thirst while in the hole, the Serpent Whisperers belive that is the will of Grihoo.

Lashes. The creature is tied to the Serpents Statue at the center of the village and all of its armor is removed. The creature is then given 1d4 x 5 lashes carried out by Dexece using a barbed whip. Each lash deals 1d4 + 4 slashing damage. A creature whose hit points are reduced to 0 from the lashes must make a DC 5 Constitution saving throw. On a failed saving throw, the creature dies from its wounds. This is the will of Grihoo. A creature who succeeds on their saving throw drops to 1 hit point instead but suffers two levels of exhaustion. Dexece may use a different weapon to carry out the lashes against Large or larger creatures, creatures with natural armor, or those who commit particularly severe violations.

Random Encounters

The Random Village Encounters table in the right column is useful for adventures based around Grihoo village. These encounters help breathe life into the village as well as generate hooks for the GM and the players to follow. Check for a random encounter

Random Village Encounters.

d12 + d8	Encounter
2	A pair of **needleblast boas*** start fighting each other in the streets. The villagers have trouble calming the beasts.
3	A celebration occurs in the village, marking a special occasion celebrated by the Serpent Whisperers.
4	1d4 + 1 Serpent Whisperers (**amazon warriors***) start brawling in the street.
5	The characters witness 1d4 + 1 **amazon warriors*** harassing Vuda and her tigers chanting "firemind" in Draconic.
6	A Serpent Whisperer (**amazon warrior***) challenges one or more of the characters to a fist fight.
7	One of the Serpent Whisperer children takes an interest in one or more of the characters. The child follows them everywhere they go.
8	The adventurers find the corpse of a Serpent Whisperer.
9-11	One of the Serpent Whisperers approaches the characters with a specific task. Roll or choose one of the tasks detailed in the Side Quests section on page 82.
12	A drunk Serpent Whisperer (**amazon warrior***) start lobbing insults the characters way.
13	A fire breaks out, and the characters have a chance to help put out the flames before the fire spreads.
14	The characters find a random trinket. See Chapter 5 of the *PHB* for random trinkets.
15	One of the **serpent guard*** or **Heirs of Kong*** harasses one or more of the characters.
16	A thief (**spy**) tries to steal from a random character. Compare the character's passive Wisdom (Perception) score to the thief's Dexterity (Sleight of Hand) check to determine if the character catches the thief in the act.
17	One of the older Serpent Whisperers has died. The others prepare a funeral pyre for her.
18	A barrel of supplies slips from a Serpent Whisperer's hands and rolls toward the character. If the characters stop the barrel before it breaks, the owner is grateful.
19	The characters witness another Serpent Whisperer (**amazon warrior***) doing something shady such as stealing from another Serpent Whisperer or breaking one of the laws.
20	One of the Serpent Whisperers (**amazon warrior**) breaks into song, an old tune from Elsath. Others stop to listen.

*See Appendix D for details.

at least once per day, and once at night if the characters are out and about. Reroll the result if it doesn't make sense given the time of day.

At your discretion, how the characters handle (or don't handle) these encounters may improve the Serpent Whisperers' attitude towards them. For example, putting out a fire might earn the characters a +5 bonus to their Earning Trust rolls. Meanwhile, finding a body or accusing a Serpent Whisperer of a crime might end up harming the characters' reputation.

Grihoo Village Trade Goods

Armor.

Item	Trade Value
Breastplate	400
Hide	10
Leather	20
Padded	10
Shield	10
Studded Leather	45

Weapons.

Item	Trade Value
Blowgun	10
Club	1
Dagger	4
Greatclub	2
Handaxe	10
Javelin	2
Net	2
Light hammer	4
Longbow	50
Macuahuitl	15
Quarterstaff	1
Shortbow	25
Sling	2
Spear	2
Tepoztopilli	25
Whip	4

Tools.

Item	Trade Value
Carpenter's tools	20
Herbalism kit	5
Jeweler's tools	25
Leatherworker's tools	10
Musical instrument (drum, flute, or shawm)	5
Smith's Tools	5
Weaver's tools	2
Woodcarver's tools	2

New Weapons

Two new optional weapons are offered below. Both are consider martial weapons.

A **machuahuitl** is a 3-foot long club lined with obsidian glass that weighs approximately 5 pounds. The weapon deals 1d6 bludgeoning or slashing damage (attacker's choice) on a hit and has the versatile property (1d8). It costs 25 gp in most markets.

A **tepoztopilli** is a polearm with a thick, blunt head at its top. It weighs approximately 5 pounds. The weapon deals 1d8 bludgeoning damage on a hit and has the reach and versatile (1d10) properties. It costs 50 gp in most markets.

Ammunition.

Item	Trade Value
Arrows (20)	2
Blowgun needles (50)	2
Sling bullets (100)	100

Adventuring Gear.

Item	Trade Value
Backpack	4
Basket	1
Bed Furs	2
Blanket	1
Bucket	1
Candle	1
Chest	10
Clothes	1
Flask	1
Hammer	2
Hunting Trap	10
Jug	1
Ladder	2
Pole (10-foot)	1
Pouch	1
Quiver	2
Rations (1 day)	1
Rope, hempen (50 feet)	2
Sack	1
Shovel	4
Tent, two-person	4
Waterskin	1
Whestone	1

Grihoo Variant: Creating Your Own Village

If you wish to create your own variation of the village presented in this adventure, use the following rules listed below.

Village Attitude

First, roll or choose an attitude on the Village Attitude table, then roll on the appropriate table to determine the nature of the village's inhabitants.

Village Attitude.

d6	Attitude
1	Friendly
2-3	Neutral
4-6	Hostile

Friendly Village.

d8	Race
1-5	Humans
6	Halflings
7	Lizardfolk
8	Wood Elves

Neutral Village.

d6	Race
1-2	Humans
3	Halflings
4-5	Lizardfolk
6	Wood Elves

Hostile Village.

d10	Race
1	Humans
2	Gnolls
3	Halflings
4	Kobolds
5-8	Lizardfolk
9	Orcs
10	Wood Elves

Population

The village is home to 5d8 **commoners**. They are protected by 3d6 **tribal warriors** led by a **berserker**. Additional NPCs may be present based on the results of the Village Notable Traits table on the next page.

village, Additionally, it gives suggestions for the village's leader. After you determine the village's leader, roll for the ruler's status on the table below.

Ruler's Status.

d20	Ruler
1-5	Respected, fair, and just
6-8	Feared tyrant
9	Weakling manipulated by the village's strongest warriors
10	Weakling manipulated by the village's wealthiest members
11	Under the influence of a powerful monster or other fiend
12	Contested leadership; open fighting
13	Given leadership by a prophecy
14	Despises the role of leader
15	Physically weak or ill
16	Outsider of the village who seized the position by force
17-18	Rules by might but respected
19-20	Religious leader

Disposition

Finally, choose or roll on the Village Disposition table to determine what events are happening in the village when the characters arrive. Each disposition is described after the table. If you roll no special disposition, the village is under no unusual stress and reacts based on its attitude.

Vilage Disposition.

d10	Disposition
1	Diseased
2	Civil unrest
3	Emergency
4	Help with a threat
5-10	No special disposition

Diseased. Roll percentile dice The result reveals the percentage of the villagers infected with a disease of your choice from Chapter 8 of the DMG. When the characters arrive in the village, the villagers beg or demand help with the infection.

Civil unrest. Multiple factions vie for control of the village. The village leaders approach the characters, asking or demanding help quelling the uprising, or the leaders of the uprising request aid with their coup or attempt to trick the characters into killing the village leaders.

Village Notable Traits.

d20	Trait
1	The village is built on stilts in a swamp. The swamp's waters are protected by 1d10 **alligators**. The village leader is a **druid**.
2	The center of the village hosts a massive monument of the village's patron god. The village leader is a **druid**.
3	A grand, stone temple is at the center of the village. The village leader is a **priest**.
4	The village is highly militaristic. They possess twice as many **tribal warriors** and are led by a **gladiator**.
5	Orchards and vegetable gardens surround the village. 1d6 + 1 **treants** and 1d4 **dryads** protect the village. The village leader is a **druid**.
6	A rushing stream divides the town. The village's leader, a **mage**, can call forth 1d4 **water elementals** to protect the village.
7	The village acts as a trade center for many of the island's inhabitants. There are many different factions at work within the village, each with their own leader all of whom are **commoners**.
8	A scientific expedition calls the village their home and are respected (or even worshipped) by the locals. The expedition consists of 1d6 **nobles**.
9	The village's inhabitants wear lavish costumes decorated with gold and precious stones. The village leader is a **commoner**.
10	The villagers are poor, diseased, and hungry. They seemingly have no leader.
11	The bodies of the dead decorate the village; it is clear that the villagers eat the flesh of humanoids. Instead of the normal protectors, the village is protected by 1d10 **berserkers**. The village leader is a **gladiator**.
12	The village is built around a vast source of wealth such as a mithril mine, healing crystals that sprout from the ground, or even a great treasure vault. The village leader is a **commoner**.
13	The village is recovering from a recent battle. Their leader was slain in battle and their most powerful warriors are fighting over who should lead the village next.
14	Magic acts strangely within the village. Any time a spell is cast near the village, roll a d20. On a result of 1, a wild magic surge occurs (as detailed in the section on sorcerers in the *PHB*). The village leader is a **commoner**.
15	The villagers protect a source of powerful knowledge. The village's leader, a **druid**, refuses to let it fall into the wrong hands.
16	Any creature that practices a religion other than that of the village is marked for death. The leader of the village is a **berserker**.
17	The chief of the village was killed by a demon some time ago. The demon has since assumed the form of the chief. The villagers live in fear.
18	The villagers coexist with a large human military force. The leader of the humans is a **knight** who leads 1d6 **veterans** and 5d6 **guards**.
19	The tomb of a powerful ancient being is hidden below the village. The villagers fiercely guard the tomb's secrets. The village leader is a **tribal warrior**.
20	The village was built atop ruins. It may even be the entrance to an ancient dungeon. The village leader is a **commoner**.

Emergency. The village is experiencing a crisis. The villagers beg or demand the characters' help in the matter. Choose or roll for an emergency on the Village emergency table below:

Village Emergency.

d4	Emergency
1	All of the villagers are missing.
2	The village is on fire.
3	The village has no food or water.
4	The village is under attack.

Help with a Threat. A deadly force from outside the village threatens the villagers' way of life. The villagers demand or beg the characters to help them with the matter. Choose or roll for the type of threat the villager's face below:

Village Threat.

d6	Threat
1-3	A deadly monster
4-5	A rival village
6	A strong military force Ω

The Skeleton Key: Island Exploration

The Skeleton Key is an island of mystery that boasts all manner of adventure, intrigue, and of course, danger. While many of the encounters are tailored to characters of 3rd level, there are a few that may be more dangerous than others. Choosing to fight or flee can make the difference between life or death for the party. You can play the encounters as hardcore as you like, pulling no punches, or you can withdraw where needed. For each day that the party explores the island, follow the rules detailed in this supplement.

How to Use This Resource

Island Exploration is used in conjunction with the *Grihoo* adventure module. Some of the elements in the adventure can also be used in your own adventures, including the points of interest, methods of escape, and random encounter tables.

Exploring The Skeleton Key

Follow these steps to explore the island.

1. Using the player's map of The Skeleton Key included in Appendix E, **identify the hex** in which the party is currently located (likely, they all start at the crash site or Grihoo village). Don't share this information with the players if the party is lost. Otherwise, show the players the party's location by pointing to the appropriate hex on their map of The Skeleton Key.
2. Let the players determine which **direction** the exploration party wants to go and whether the party plans to move at a **normal pace**, a **fast pace**, or a **slow pace**. One of the characters must be the navigator.
3. Each day, make a Wisdom (Survival) check on the navigator's behalf to **determine if the party becomes lost**.

4. Also, **roll for random encounters** throughout the day and check for food consumption.
5. Optional: The forest is relatively easy to **forage** in, requiring a DC 10 Wisdom (Survival) check to secure food and water (see chapter 5 of the *PHB* for details).

Travel Distances

On the map of the Skeleton Key overleaf, each hex measures 3 miles across and is considered difficult terrain.

Normal Pace. Characters moving at a normal pace can travel 4 hexes per day.

Fast Pace. If the characters move at a fast pace, you can increase the number of hexes they are able to move by 1 per day. Characters moving at a fast pace take a -5 penalty to their passive Wisdom (Perception) scores, making them more likely to miss clues and walk into ambushes.

Slow Pace. If characters set a slow pace, they can only travel 3 hexes per day. Characters moving at a slow pace can move stealthily. As long as they're in the open, they can try to surprise or sneak by other creatures they encounter.

Tracking Miles. If you prefer to track miles, you may do so. Travel times are then 18 miles per day at a normal pace, 24 miles per day at a fast pace, or 12 miles per day at a slow pace.

Flying Speeds. A character with a flying speed of 30 feet can travel 4 miles per hour.

Navigation

At the start of the task, the GM makes a Wisdom (Survival) check on behalf of the navigator. The result of the check determines whether or not the explorers become lost over the course of the day.

Difficulty. The DC of the check is based on the day's most common terrain:
- DC 10 for fields and coasts

- DC 15 for forests and mountains
- Apply a +5 bonus to the check if the group sets a slow pace for the day
- Apply a -5 penalty if the group is moving at a fast pace.

Success. If the check succeeds, the navigator knows exactly where the explorers are on the player's map of The Skeleton Key throughout the day.

Failure. If the check fails, the party becomes lost.
- Each hex on the map is surrounded by six other hexes; whenever a lost party moves 1 hex, roll a d6 to randomly determine which neighboring hex the party enters, and do not divulge the party's location to the players.
- While the party is lost, players can't pinpoint the group's location on their map of The Skeleton Key.
- The next time a navigator succeeds on a Wisdom (Survival) check made to navigate, reveal the party's actual location to the players.

Random Encounters

Outside of a few major locations noted on the GM's map overleaf, The Skeleton Key is an open sandbox for the characters to discover monsters, hidden locations, and other interesting hooks during their time on the island.

Check for a random encounter in the morning, afternoon, and evenings. Roll 1d20; an encounter occurs on a 16 or higher. Place the encounter at a range that makes sense. The majority of the encounters described are fierce monsters and creatures who have evolved to become hunters. Encounters marked with an asterisk are described below.

Heads of Grihoo. See the section on Grihoo Holes below.

The Serpent Whisperers. The characters run into a hunting party of the Serpent Whisperers of Grihoo. There is a 50% chance that Ykyope is leading the party. The outcome of the encounter depends on the character's current relationship with the Serpent Whisperers.

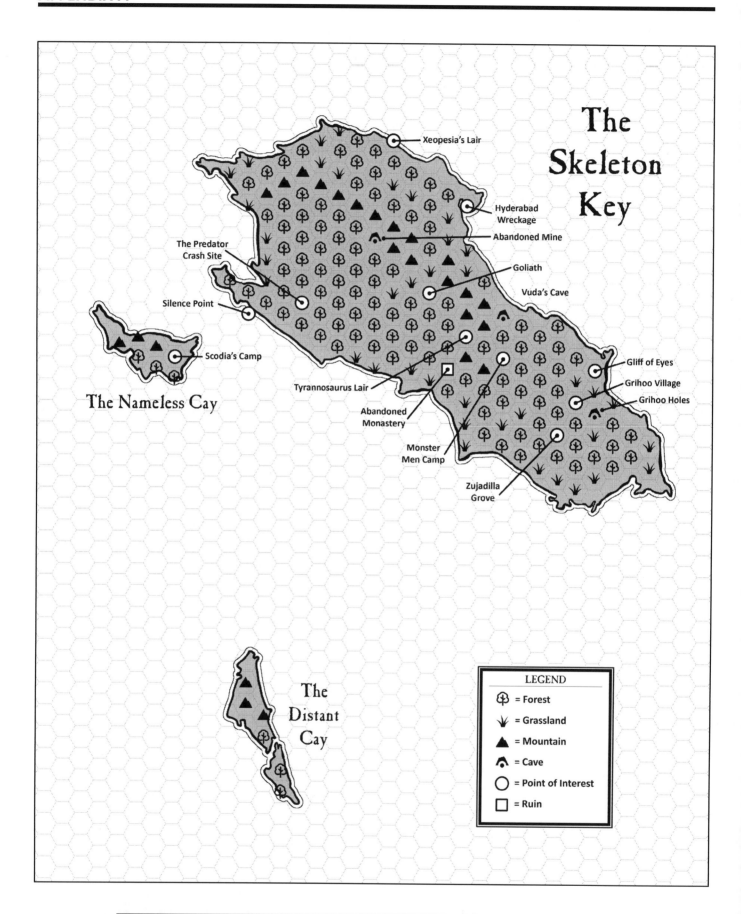

The Skeleton Key

Xeopesia's Lair

Hyderabad Wreckage

Abandoned Mine

The Predator Crash Site

Goliath

Vuda's Cave

Silence Point

Scodia's Camp

Gliff of Eyes

Grihoo Village

Grihoo Holes

The Nameless Cay

Tyrannosaurus Lair

Abandoned Monastery

Monster Men Camp

Zujadilla Grove

The Distant Cay

LEGEND
= Forest
= Grassland
= Mountain
= Cave
= Point of Interest
= Ruin

Locations on the Skeleton Key

The map depicts The Skeleton Key and its surrounding islands with key locations marked. The key locations are described below, presented in alphabetical order for ease of reference.

Random Encounters.

100	Encounter
01-05	1d6 + 2 **giant bats**
06-09	1d2 **panthers**
10-15	1d4 **poison snakes**
16-19	2d8 **baboons**
20-28	1d6 + 3 **hyenas**
29-34	1 **hawk**
35-39	1d4 + 1 **giant lizards**
40-49	Heads of Grihoo*
50-54	1d6 + 2 **boars**
55-59	1 **ape**
60-63	1 **tiger**
64-65	3d6 **flying snakes**
66-70	4d4 **kobolds**
71-74	1d3 **constrictor snakes**
75-80	1d10 + 5 **giant rats**
81-85	1d8 + 1 **giant frogs**
86-87	3d6 **stirges**
88-00	Serpent Whisperers of Grihoo*

Abandoned Mine

While the characters are exploring the island near the nameless mountain range, they discover a mine, abandoned for a century or longer. Hiding inside the mine are two mysterious people.

Area Information. This area has the following general features.

Dimensions & Terrain. The abandoned mine player handout map is included in Appendix E. When the characters find the mine, read:

> Pushing past trees, you come upon what looks like an old mining fort in the side of a cliff, probably a few decades old, consumed by the aggressive flora of the jungle. The

> crude, timber portcullis that once blocked entry into the mine rests against the stone pillars at either side of it. You doubt that it's still operational, but it looks like one can squeeze between the timbers were one so inclined.

Lighting. If the characters approach in the day time, the entrance to the mine itself is well lit by the sun above.

Creature Information. Hiding inside the mine are **Man** and **Boy**. Unless the characters were particularly stealthy as they approached the mine, Man is waiting inside the mine, standing just a few feet to the north of the entrance into the mine. Meanwhile, Boy is hiding closer to the northern tower. The stats for Man and Boy are detailed at in Appendix D.

Objectives and Goals. Man and Boy are on the run from the Serpent Whisperers of Grihoo. Once Man recognizes that the characters are not the Serpent Whisperers, he will attempt to make a truce with the characters. Read the following:

> The man backs away and lowers his weapon. You get a good look at him. His clothing is a hodgepodge of random armor, leather, and animal furs. The exposed parts of his flesh reveal dark, scarred skin. He hides his face behind the cowl of a bronze helmet. His beard is dark and kinky, touching his chest.
>
> "I do not wish to fight. Boy and I only wish to escape the Serpent Whisperers."
>
> A boy steps out from the darkness behind the man. No older than 10, the boy is thin, exhausted-looking and wearing only a tan loincloth. He has dark eyes, dark skin, and a mess of kinky, black hair on top of his head. If you didn't know any better, you'd guess he was a Dinzer.

What Do They Know? Man and Boy both know the location of the Temple of Grihoo. While they will not travel with the characters to that end of the island, they can provide directions. They warn that there are nearly one hundred warriors that live at the Temple of Grihoo. In addition to the warriors, the Temple is guarded by massive, intelligent apes known as the Heirs of Kong.

Treasure. Among the building supplies found in the abandoned mine, the characters can discover *gloves of amphibios*. See Appendix C for details.

Cliff of Eyes

Roughly four miles north of Grihoo Village is a clearing that overlooks the sea. This cliff is featured in the adventure **Grihoo**, as the landing site for Theo Barbakis' crew.

Area Description. The cliff has the following features.

Dimensions & Terrain. The cliff sits overlooking the island's eastern coastline 100-feet below. The grass here is tall, and depending on the season, there may be plenty of wildflowers, too. The tree-line is approximately 150 feet from the cliff's edge.

Light. Thanks to the lack of trees by the cliff, this is one of the brightest (and most beautiful spots) on the entire island.

Skulls. Despite its beauty, the Cliff of Eyes harbors a dark secret. Whenever male infants are born of Serpent Whisperer mothers, the Serpent Whisperers carry the unwanted children to this cliff and cast them into the waters far below. There are hints at this gruesome ritual at the rocks far below.

Windy. The wind coming off the water of the Ocean of Warna blasts the clearing. Although it's not strong enough to affect ranged combat or flyers, it does make hearing difficult. All creatures in the clearing have a -5 to Wisdom (Perception) checks that rely on hearing.

The Distant Cay

Roughly 36 miles south of The Skeleton Key is a small pair of islands collectively known as The Distant Cay. Because it is not easily seen from The Skeleton Key, the Serpent Whisperers of Grihoo hardly know it exists. No humanoids live on The Distant Cay. The island is home to shipwrecks, cackling gulls, and turtles.

Goliath

Of the nameless mountain range's three volcanoes, Goliath is the largest; hence the name. Fortunately, it's been over 200 years since the monstrous mountain blew its top and spilled lava into the valley. The Serpent Whisperers' ancestors recall the last explosion, nicknaming the event "The Fire Time." To add to the ominous event, the first Serpent Whisperer with firemind was born shortly after the eruption.

Despite its dormant state, Goliath is still home to creatures from the Burn who escaped their plane. Serpent Whisperers have come across fire elementals, magmin, and even salamanders in the area. While the characters are in goliath's hex, Random Encounters occur on a result of 15-20. Use the Goliath Random Encounters table below to determine the nature of the encounter. Creatures marked with an asterisk are detailed in Appendix D.

Goliath Random Encounters.

1d8	Encounter
1	1 **basilisk**
2	1 **earth elemental**
3	1 **fire elemental**
4	1 **chimera**
5	2d4 **magma mephits**
6	1d4 **lava cobras***
7	1d6 **magmin**
8	1 **salamander**

The Portal. One of the ways to escape the island is through the small portal in the area. A creature proficient in Arcana as well as any creature that can cast druid or sorcerer spells can sense the presence of the portal when they enter the hex. The creature can make a DC 13 Wisdom (Arcana) check to track the portal's location. On a successful check, the discover the portal. The portal leads to a random plane of existence. Use the Portals table below to determine where the portal takes someone who enters it. The portal's destination changes every 6 seconds.

There is no way of telling what is on the other side of a portal. What happens to the characters after they set through the portal is ultimately up to you.

Portals.

d20	Plane of Existence
1	The Burn
2	The Construct
3	The Chaos
4	The Cruel
5	The Crumble
6	The Dark
7	The Depth
8	The Dream
9	The Inevitable
10	The Other
11	The Void
12-19	A random pocket dimension.
20	The Real

Grihoo Holes

When the characters find this area, read or paraphrase the following:

> The trees break, revealing a small clearing. All over the jungle floor, you see a dozen or more strange, 1-foot diameter holes spaced roughly 5 feet apart.

The holes are deep; potentially hundreds of feet or more. Unless the characters somehow reduce their size to Tiny, they won't be able to go into the holes. When the characters find the holes, there is a 20% chance that 1d4 + 2 Heads of Grihoo emerge from the holes and attack. The Heads of Grihoo are detailed in Chapter 8 of the Grihoo adventure module.

In the Rescue Pheice side quest in the Grihoo Village section, the characters will find Pheice here standing on a rock.

Grihoo Village

Grihoo Village is detailed earlier in this Appendix.

Monster Men Camp

Man and Boy (see *Abandoned Mine*) weren't the first men to escape the Temple of Grihoo. Over the years, escaped men have fled into the southern edge of the nameless mountain range. Adding to their ranks are the few rescued male infants of which the Serpent Whisperers dispose of after they are born.

The men get the "Monster Men" moniker from the paint they wear to camouflage themselves while hunting. Further protecting the men from the notice of the Serpent Whisperers is the presence of Claw, the tyrannosaurus rex that plagues the region to the southwest. Viothye knows that once Claw is killed, the women will be able to reclaim the men.

Area Description. A map of the camp is on the next page. The Monster Men camp has the following features:

Dimensions & Terrain. The camp is well hidden in a copse of lush jungle trees. There are six thatch-roofed bamboo huts, each with seven-foot-high ceilings and dirt floors. The men keep a small fire at the center of the village but work hard to ensure that the smoke isn't noticeable by the Serpent Whisperers. A narrow path at the northeastern end of the village leads to a cave in the mountains if the camp comes under attack.

Hen House. The men were fortunate enough to secure a few wild hens and a rooster on a hunt. They've preserved the animals in a cage at the

MONSTER MEN VILLAGE

1 square = 5 feet

patreon.com/tomcartos

western side of the village.

Huts. Each of the huts contains one or more beds and crates, barrels, or other containers to store food. The men have very few possessions, but each hut has 2d4 random trinkets inside. The trinkets are crafted by the men or found in the jungle.

Creature Information. The camp is led by Eighty-two (NG male human **tribal warrior**), an escaped male slave. With him are seven other men (all N male human **tribal warriors**) and three boys (human non-combatants). All eight of the adults look exactly the same, except they vary in age (they're clones). The boys are the sons of Man (see the Abandoned Mine section).

What Do They Want? Ultimately, the men want to be left alone. While they are bitter toward the Serpent Whisperers for their treatment and enslavement, they recognize that they are in no position to combat the women directly. If confronted, however, Eighty-two and half of the men will protect the other men while they flee further into the mountains with the boys. Eighty-two and his men aren't trained fighters, but they are passionate and will fight to until the death.

What Do They Know? The men have limited memories of their time before they were slaves to the Grihoo. Eighty-two recalls a few details of that time: a room where he and others like him huddled together for

safety, a masked figure in all white who gave him food, monsters screaming in the dark. Eighty-two believes that the temple hides many secrets, secrets that are important to the entire world. And he knows that Viothye and the others will kill to protect those secrets.

The Nameless Cay

West of The Skeleton is The Nameless Cay, a 16-mile long island visible only from Silence Point. The exile Scodia makes her camp here.

Ocean of Warna

Known for its calm waves and mesmerizing sunrises, the Ocean of Warna completely surrounds The Skeleton Keys and its neighboring islands. From The Skeleton Key, the eastern coast of Omeria rests 500 miles across Warna's waves.

The Predator Crash Site

The Predator was a converted Dinzer warblimp carrying rare animals from the ruins of Qola to Knotside. Sabotaged by a terrorist hellbent on destroying the Omerian nation of Odonburg, the ship crash-landed on the western edge of the island.

The Predator is featured in the first two parts of this adventure series, **The Flight of the Predator** and **The Skeleton Key**.

Ruined Monastery

At the southern edge of the nameless mountains, an ancient monastery created by the Disciples of Ze (an extinct race of birdfolk) stands ominously at the center of a misty chasm.

Area Information. The ruined monastery is built onto a pillar that stands at the center of a chasm that is 60-feet wide and 100-feet deep.

Dimensions & Terrain. Atop the pillar is an ancient monastery flanked by two, 120-foot tall statues of bird-humanoids. An ancient bridge of thick vines once connected the monastery to the southern end of the chasm. The bridge is now broken. If the characters make it to the other side of the bridge, they find three abandoned pagodas.

Light. Mist obscures the majority of the temple itself. Otherwise, the amount of light in the area depends on the time of day and weather

Right & Left Pagodas. Both the leftmost and rightmost pagodas are empty. Anything of value that was once within the buildings have long since been removed.

Central Pagoda. The center building is empty as well, except large, broken stones litter the floor.

Broken Tablet. A character who succeeds on a DC 10 Intelligence (Investigation) check identifies that

Scodia's Traps.

d4	Trap
1	**Falling Logs.** A character triggers a tripwire that releases logs. Each of the characters must succeed on a DC 13 Dexterity saving throw, or take 2d6 bludgeoning damage from the falling logs.
2	**Poison Dart.** A character triggers a tripwire that fires a dart. The dart makes a +6 attack against the character. On a hit, the dart deals 1 piercing damage plus 2d7 damage. The character must succeed on a DC 15 Constitution saving throw, or become poisoned for 24 hours.
3	**Snare.** A character steps on a snare. The character is grappled and restrained and lifted 30 feet into the air. The character can cut the rope grappling their foot by dealing 2 slashing damage to the rope.
4	**Spike Pit.** A character steps onto a covered pit trap. The character falls 10 feet down into the pit and takes 1d6 damage from the fall and 2d4 piercing damage from the spikes. This trap cannot be disabled, only avoided.

the stones had once made up a tablet and the tablet once bore a symbol that looked like a star made of tangled serpents. If a character spends 10 minutes trying to reassemble the tablet and succeed on a DC 12 Intelligence check to do so, they also recognize that there had once been a secret compartment hidden in the center of the tablet. Whatever was there is now gone.

Dead Knight. Ancient, rusted breastplate armor bearing the sigil of the god Ilwyn (a helmet with a sunrise behind it) can be found in the sand in front of the pagodas. Just a few feet from the armor is a sword of Pressonian make. A character who succeeds on a DC 15 Intelligence (His-

tory or smith's tools) check recognizes that the sword is probably at least 400 years old.

Treasure. The discarded sword found in the sand is a *+1 longsword*. The sword was originally the sword of Sir Gozwik and is the very item Theo Barbakis claims to be searching for. See the **Grihoo** adventure for details.

Scodia's Camp

Six years ago, Viothye's sister, Scodia, murdered another of the Serpent Whisperers. She avoided death by choosing exile as her punishment. Carrying the brand of exile, she fled north to Silent Cove and sailed on a canoe over the small channel connecting The Skeleton Key and The Name-

less Cay. There she's lived in peace ever since.

Area Description. Scodia's Camp has the following features.

Dimensions & Terrain. Scodia's camp is a bamboo lean-to built among the trees on the western end of the island. There is a small table and a few crates to hold Scodia's possessions, mostly items she gathers along the coastline. Scodia sleeps in a hammock between two trees. If the weather turns poor (which it frequently does, thanks to Warna), Scodia has a small cave a mile from her camp to which she can retreat.

Canoe. Scodia keeps a canoe in her camp. She uses it whenever she needs to return to The Skeleton Key. There is only enough room in the canoe for her and Nup-up.

Nup-nup. Nup-nup, a **boar**, acts as Scodia's "guard" and friend. Nup-nup is aggressive and as friendly as a housecat. Scodia's relationship with Nup-nup turned her away from meat and toward vegetarianism years ago.

Traps. The hex surrounding Scodia's camp is littered with traps to prevent the invasion of Serpent Whisperers, pirates, or anyone else who would hope to challenge her. Every hour the characters spend on The Nameless Cay, roll a d20. On a result of 15 or higher, they stumble into one of her traps. Choose a trap or role randomly on Scodia's Traps table below. Noticing the traps requires a successful DC 15 passive Wisdom (Perception) check. A trap can be disabled with a successful DC 13 Dexterity check using proficiency with thieves' tools.

Creature Information. Scodia (CG amazon warrior) is a gray-haired woman in her mid-60s. She bears a scar in the shape of a hydra over her forehead—the mark of an exile— which she uses a bandana to conceal. When the characters find Scodia, her arm is in a sling. She injured herself while building her raft. As such, all of her attacks are made at disadvan-

tage.

What Does She Want? Scodia just wants to live in peace. Years ago, she disagreed with her sister Viothye on their treatment of the men who came from the temple. This led to her exile. She harbors no ill-will towards the other Serpent Whisperers but believes that they are foolish, stubborn, and too conservative for their own good. She hopes to escape the island someday and has even begun production on a sea-faring vessel. However, she injured herself during production and needs help completing it.

What Does She Know? Scodia knows many of the Serpent Whisperers' darkest secrets. A former key-holder herself, she knows that the key that Viothye holds grants access to the lower layers of the temple. Although she's never gone further than the second sub-level, she shares that there was all manner of terrible monstrosities who lived there. She also knows that the Serpent Whisperers kill all non-female infants, casting them into the sea at the Cliff of Eyes. She suspects, however, that there is a contingent of men whom the Serpent Whisperers have dubbed "the Monster Men" who have rescued a few of the infants.

Scodia's Raft. Scodia has built half of a raft with a sail capable of holding three to four people. Unfortunately, she injured her arm and hasn't been able to complete it. If the characters assist Scodia, she offers to take two of them from the island with her and Nup-nup.

Helping Scodia requires two work-weeks worth of effort (no rolls required). Since they are off the main island, it's unlikely The Serpent Whisperers will catch them in the act.

Silence Point

Silence Point is a long, gravel-ridden sandbar that stretches points toward The Nameless Cay. On a clear day, The Nameless Cay is visible from Silence Point. And if the characters look

across the water at night, they might even see a light from Scodia's fire (see Scodia's Camp).

Tyrannosaurus Lair

A vicious **tyrannosaurus rex** named Claw makes its home in a jagged, overgrown canyon littered with animal bones. More intelligent than most of its kind (Claw's Intelligence score is 4), Claw is an expert at setting up ambushes for hunters and other creatures who hope to bring the tyrannosaurus down.

Vuda's Cave

When the fireminded Serpent Whisperer Vuda needs to hide or collect her thoughts, she flees to a small cave north of the village in the mountains. Vuda's Cave is featured in the *Grihoo* adventure module. A map of the cave is featured above.

Xeopesia's Lair

Xeopesia is a dangerous **medusa** who lives north of Grihoo Village in a small cavern overlooking the ocean. When Goliath's top last blew, Xeopesia crawled from The Crumble into The Real. She has been a constant thorn in the Serpent Whisperers' side ever since.

Area Description. A map of Xeopesia's lair is overleaf. Xeopesia's lair has the following features:

Dimensions & Terrain. Xeopesia's cavern is a high-ceilinged, smooth-walled cavern eroded by Warna's waves.

Light. The interior of Xeopesia's cavern is usually dark. She uses the shadows to hide. However, in the morning and early afternoon, the sun over the ocean illuminates the inside of the cavern.

Stone Heads. Xeopesia decorates her cavern with the petrified severed heads of all of the Serpent Whisperers' who've challenged her in the past. All of the women's faces are locked in expressions of eternal horror.

Wet Sand. The sandy floors of the cavern are soft and act as difficult terrain for any creature who does not possess proficiency in Acrobatics or Athletics. Xeopesia is unaffected.

1 - Beach. Xeopesia keeps the sands of her beach littered with brittle shells. A creature moving across the area the shells must succeed on a DC 15 Dexterity saving throw or break shells. The sound is loud enough to alert Xeopesia to the presence of intruders and give her time to prepare.

Half-buried in the sand are four headless statues. The statues were Serpent Whisperers who were hunting the medusa.

2 - Headless Statue Gallery. Three headless Serpent Whisperer statues stand in this chamber, still holding their weapons and shields. Xeopesia removed the warriors' heads and added them to her collection. If Xeopesia has time to prepare, she alerts the gargoyle Golcan. Then, Golcan pretends to be a statue and stands among the Serpent Whisperers with a surprised look on his face. Golcan waits for characters to pass him and head towards Xeopesia before he makes an attack. His favorite technique is to grab weak-looking creatures, fly them 100 feet out to the ocean and drop them in the water.

3 - Hiding Nook. If Xeopesia has time to prepare (see area 1), she grabs her weapons and hides in this cavern. Years earlier, she found a piece of mirrored glass on the beach and hung it on the wall (see the map) at the apex. She's trained herself to avoid looking at the glass directly but uses it to see into area 2. Creatures who see the glass only recognize that it's a reflection with a successful DC 13 Wisdom (Perception) check. Her petrifying gaze still works in the mirror's reflection.

4 - Golcan's Nook. Xeopesia doesn't live alone. Golcan (gargoyle), another creature who escaped the Crumble after Goliath's last eruption, lives in this chamber. Here the gargoyle eats

XEOPASIA'S LAIR

Mirrored Glass

1 square = 5 feet

SUPPORTED ON PATREON | www.DYSONLOGOS.cor

oyster shells and the occasional pearl he finds.

Treasure. If a character searches the sand in this area and succeeds on a successful DC 13 Intelligence (Investigation) check, they can find 1d4 pearls. Each pearl is worth 100 gp in a mainland market.

5 - Wall of Heads. Acting as a partition between the lower section of Xeopesia's cavern and her chambers is a wall made of heads. In addition to the Serpent Whisperer heads, there are the heads of men, many of which she collected from a scientific exploration ship unlucky enough to discover the medusa a century ago.

6 - Xeopesia's Chamber. If the characters manage to catch Xeopesia off guard, she is found reading in her chambers. A hundred years ago,

a ship full of scientists ran aground near her cavern. She killed all the scientists and stole the ship's cargo. Many of those items remain in this area.

Treasure. Xeopesia's chamber has four crates each with 50 books; a small, wooden treasure chest containing 2,002 gp; a spyglass which is still in excellent condition; a bronze *horn of Valhalla*; and *no-stones* (see Appendix C for details).

Zujadilla Grove
While the sweet-tasting purple-and-yellow striped fruit known as zujadilla grows all over most of The Skeleton Key and its neighboring islands, this area, in particular, has plenty of zujadilla. If the characters discover this grove while hunting for zujadilla for Toumida (see Side

Quests in the Grihoo Village section), they can collect as many zujadilla as they can carry (10 is all that Toumida wants, however, 10 zujadillas have a trade value of 1).

Escaping the Skeleton Key

One of the downtime activity options offered the characters in the *Grihoo* adventure module involves finding a method to escape the island. There are three main ways to escape the island, each one described in detail below: building a raft, signaling a ship, and finding a portal.

Building a Raft

The character can build their own raft or they can assist Scodia with completing hers. Once a raft is built, the characters must sail from the island. To sail away from the island, use the following rules.

Getting Past the Breaking Waves. The first challenge the characters face is getting over the waves that break near the islands' coastline. Each character must make a group Strength (Athletics) check. Refer to the Breaking Waves table below to determine how successful the characters are in getting past the waves. Once past the waves, the characters are free to sail over the Ocean of Warna.

Set Course. The raft travels at a speed of 1 1/2 miles per hour, or 36 miles per day. There are three directions the characters can travel from the island to reach land.

- The Dragonborn island of Aegreya is approximately 700 miles north of The Skeleton Key. It will take the characters 20 days to reach Aegreya's coast.
- Omeria's eastern shoreline is 600 miles west of The Skeleton Key. It will take the characters 17 days to reach Omeria.
- The large island of Elsath is approximately 850 miles south of The Skeleton Key, 24 days away.

Navigating the Ocean. Have the players designate one party member

Breaking Waves.

Outcome	Loot
Total Failure	The ship is capsized and crushed against the waves. The characters must swim back to shore which is 1d4 x 100 feet away.
Failure	A setback occurs and there's still work to be done. The characters must make another group check, but this time with disadvantage on all of their checks.
Success	The characters make progress, but they still have some work to do. The characters must make another group check, but this time, with advantage on their checks.
Total Success	The characters successful get past the waves.

as the navigator. The navigator might be an NPC, such as Scodia. The party can switch its navigator day-to-day.

At the start of each new travel day, the GM makes a Wisdom (Survival) check on behalf of the navigator. The result of the check determines whether or not the party becomes lost over the course of the day. The DC for the check is 10 for clear weather, 15 if there is light rain, or 20 if there is heavy rain. See Chapter 5 of the DMG for details on weather.

If the check succeeds, the Navigator maintains the ship's course. If the check fails, it will take the raft an additional 1d10 days to reach its destination. Do not let the players know that time has been added to their travel time.

Signaling a Ship

Although it's rare that ships pass close enough to The Skeleton Key and

its neighboring islands for someone to signal them, it does occasionally happen.

The easiest way to signal a ship is by creating a large bonfire. Maintaining a bonfire requires 8 continuous hours of work from at least one character.

Smoke from a bonfire can be seen at a distance of 20 miles at sea. For every eight hours that the characters maintain a bonfire, roll a d20. On a result of 20, a ship notices the characters' bonfire. The nature of the ship is up to the GM, it can be a passing pirate ship, Aegreyan slaver ship, or even a Dinzer aircraft.

Finding the Portal

When Goliath erupted two hundred years ago, it tore a hole in reality. While the hole has mostly healed itself, a small sliver remains. See *Goliath* earlier for details on the Portal. Ω

Dramatis Personae: Grihoo

The notable NPCs that appear in *Grihoo* are listed below in alphabetical order for your convenience. Included on the table are their stat block references and where you can find them. *MM* stands for the Fifth Edition core manual of monster stat blocks and *Appendix D* is included in this book.

Character Reference Table.

Character	Description	Stat Block (Reference)
Theo Barbakis	A danaavrakt in disguise as a Pressonian noble	**rakshasa** (*MM*)
Gar	Sixty-six's shield guardian	**shield guardian** (*MM*)
Gozwik	A deceased Pressonian knight	—
Grihoo	The superhydra upon which the temple was built	See Part 8
Kathoraad	One of the temple's guardians	**stone golem** (*MM*)
Maf	A dulon, one of the progenitors of all life on Casar	—
Odon	The founder of the magocratic nation of Odonburg	—
Qiu Xiang	An Aegreyan/Pressonian paladin employed by Barbakis	LE dragonborn **knight** (*MM*)
Rain in the Moonlight	A sorcerer employed by Barbakis	NE devilkin **sorcerer** (*Appendix D*)
Sixty-six	A centuries-old clone	N **cloned sorcerer** (*Appendix D*)
Vision of the Water	A sorcerer employed by Barbakis	NE devilkin **sorcerer** (*Appendix D*)
Yarry	A rogue employed by Barbakis	CG halfling **spy** (*MM*)
Ykyope	A Serpent Whisperer of Grihoo	LN **amazon warrior** (*Appendix D*)
Viothye	Chief of The Serpent Whisperers	LN **amazon warrior** (*Appendix D*)
Vuda	A Serpent Whisperer of Grihoo with two tiger companions	CN **amazon warrior** (*Appendix D*) Ω

APPENDIX B
NEW PLAYER OPTIONS

BY DAVE HAMRICK
ART BY WILLIAM MCAUSLAND AND LUIGI CASTELLANI

New Character Option: Serpent Whisperer

To play a Serpent Whisperer of Grihoo, follow the normal process for character creation except with the following changes. You can work with your GM to make exceptions to any of these rules.

1 - Race

As a race of warrior women, **all Serpent Whisperers are female humans**. You're free to use either the standard human or variant human from the *PHB*. Serpent Whisperers usually speak only Draconic, so you can speak Draconic and one other language or Common and Draconic.

Optional Rule: Capitalize. Serpent Whisperers are excellent at creating combination strikes against their opponents. If you take the Variant Human option and your GM permits, you can choose to substitute your starting skill proficiency for the following feature:

Capitalize. Once per round, if you hit a creature that you can see with a melee weapon attack, you can use your bonus action to immediately make another melee weapon attack against the same creature. This extra attack has disadvantage.

2 - Class

The majority of Serpent Whisperers are made up of the following classes: barbarian, fighter, ranger, and rogue.

Serpent Whisperers have a natural fear of the supernatural and magic in particular. They do not practice religion (with the exception of worship of Grihoo and the temple itself) nor are they anywhere near a wizard's academy or bardic college. As such, the bard, cleric, and wizard classes are forbidden to Serpent Whisperers. Also, Serpent Whisperers do not follow the tenets of special oaths or monastic traditions. Therefore, they cannot be paladins or monks.

While rare, there are Serpent Whisperers who have shown sorcerous powers. There are also a few serpent whisperers who could draw power directly from the titan Grihoo and became warlocks. Druidism is not totally unheard of.

3 - Description

Most Serpent Whisperers are lawful in alignment and tend toward ethical neutrality.

While it's possible to have variations on any of the backgrounds offered in the *PHB*, Serpent Whisperers often have the hermit, outlander, or the Serpent Whisperer background detailed in the right column.

4 - Starting Equipment

When you create your character, you receive equipment based on your background. However, you do not start with the normal equipment for your class. Instead you start with trade value equal to 2d4 x 10. See the Trade Table in Appendix A for details on the goods you can purchase using your trade value.

New Player Options

The two new player options are available to Serpent Whisperer players: the Serpent Guard Martial Archetype and the Serpent Whisperer background.

Serpent Guard Archetype

At 3rd level, a Serpent Whisperer gains the Martial Archetype feature. The following Serpent Guard option is available to a Serpent Whisperer character, in addition to those offered in the *PHB*.

In a society where strength and combat prowess is a part of life, the Serpent Guard rise above their peers as the greatest and most respected (or feared) Serpent Whisperer warriors.

Weapon Crafting. When you choose this Martial Archetype at 3rd level, you gain proficiency with smith's tools.

Weapon Expertise. At 3rd level, you have trained extensively with a variety of weapons. Choose three weapons with which you are proficient. Once on your turn, when you make an attack using one of the weapons with which you are proficient, you can roll a d4 before you make the attack roll. You can then add the d4 either to the attack roll or to the damage of the attack roll (but not both).

The bonus damage's die size increases to 1d6 at 7th level and 1d8 at 18th level.

Weapon Personalization. At 7th level, you can personalize a weapon so that only you are able to use it effectively.

Serpent Guard Martial Archetype

Fighter Level	Features
3rd	Weapon Crafting, Weapon Expertise (1d4)
7th	Weapon Personalization, Weapon Mysticism
10th	Additional Fighting Style, Weapon Expertise (1d6)
15th	Combat Maneuvers
18th	Blitz, Weapon Expertise (1d8)

Using smith's tools, you spend an hour tweaking a weapon that you are proficient with. This weapon may be magical or mundane. Once the personalization process is complete, if a creature other than you attempts to make an attack using the weapon, it does so at disadvantage. In addition, you have advantage on Strength (Athletics) checks or Dexterity (Acrobatics) checks to avoid being disarmed.

You may spend another hour using smith's tools to undo the personalization benefits. Another creature may undo the personalization benefits of the weapon. However, the creature must spend 8 working hours using smith's tools returning the weapon to its previous state; at the end of the 8 hours, the creature must make a Dexterity check using smith's tools against a DC of 8 + your proficiency bonus + your Intelligence modifier. On a successful check, the weapon's personalization benefits are removed.

Weapon Mysticism. Also at 7th level, when you hit a creature with one of the weapons you chose for your Weapon Expertise feature, the weapon counts as magical for the purpose of overcoming resistance and immunity to nonmagical attacks and damage.

Additional Fighting Style. Starting at 10th level, you can choose a second option from the Fighting Style class feature.

Combat Maneuvers. At 15th level, on each of your turns in combat, you can take a bonus action so long as you don't attack more than once during your turn. The action can be used only to take the Dash, Disengage, or Dodge action.

Blitz. At 18th level, when you make an attack, you can make up to three additional attacks, provided that each attack targets a different creature this turn. Once you use this feature, you can't use it again until you complete a short or long rest.

Serpent Whisperer Background

You are a Serpent Whisperer, a warrior woman from the village of Grihoo, and have dedicated your life to the protection of The Skeleton Key and its secrets.

Skill Proficiencies: Athletics, Survival **Tool Proficiencies**: Herbalism Kit **Equipment**: A staff, trophies from an animal you killed, a set of traveler's clothes, and a pouch containing a gem worth 10 gp (or trade value of 5).

Feature: Serpent Whisperer. Through sounds and gestures, you can communicate simple ideas with snakes and other serpents. In addition, you have advantage on Animal Handling checks made against snakes and serpents.

Role. Each Serpent Whisperer is given a specific role in their society. Choose one of the following role options that best fits your character, or roll randomly on the table below:

d8	Role
1	Hunter
2	Tracker
3	Serpent Guard
4	Caretaker
5	Gardener
6	Groundskeeper
7	Trader
8	Childbearer

Suggested Characteristics. A Serpent Whisperer is raised a powerful warrior whose mission is to protect the interests of the village, the temple, and the island.

d8	Personality Trait
1	I am extremely literal and don't often joke.
2	I am slow to trust, and hate outsiders.
3	I enjoy bragging about my victories.
4	No time to think; time for action!
5	I am curious and want to understand how everything works.
6	I prefer to be alone and don't enjoy the company of others.
7	I sometimes wonder about what the world is like away from the island.
8	I prefer to communicate only with grunts and gestures.

d6	Ideal
1	**Duty.** I am bound by the laws of my community and the people in it. (Lawful)
2	**Beauty.** The world is a wonderful place, one which should be preserved. (Neutral)
3	**Might.** Only the strongest should rule. (Evil)
4	**Change.** The old ways are growing stagnant and have held back the community for far too long. (Chaotic)
5	**Glory.** I am the greatest warrior in the village and I will always try to prove it. (Any)
6	**Equality.** All creatures—even Serpent Whisperers—are created equal. (Good)

d6	Bond
1	The only thing that matters to me are my home and my family, The Serpent Whisperers.
2	The secrets in the temple art worth protecting at all costs; even if that means my own death.
3	I am madly in love with someone who does not feel the same away about me.
4	I've had dreams about a life off the island. I wish to find out what those dreams mean.
5	I have not yet found anyone who is worthy of combat.
6	I disappointed my tribe in the past. I will spend the rest of my life making up for that mistake.

d6	Flaw
1	I have strong body odor.
2	Conversations bore me to the point of tears.
3	I am quick to turn to violence.
4	My curiosity often gets me into trouble.
5	I believe that mercy is for the weak.
6	I am as stubborn as a rooster. Ω

Optional Arcane Traditions

This reference is a re-issue of an article from the out of print **Broad-Sword Monthly #1**. Newer readers may enjoy this addendum to **Pexia Academy for the Arcane Arts** from the **BroadSword Compendium Volume 1**. These experimental rules have not been playtested.

Teacher

There's an old saying, "Those who can, do; and those who can't, teach." Of course, that saying is completely erroneous when applied to those who practice the mystic arts. Wizard teachers are often considered to be some of the most powerful practitioners around. Typically, they are feared by those who recognize their relationship with magic. Wizard teachers use their coaching powers to boost other spellcasters and improve the abilities of those around them.

Magical Expertise. Starting when you choose this tradition at 2nd level, you learn two languages of your choice. You also become proficient in the Arcana and History skills.

Your proficiency bonus is doubled for any ability check you make that uses either of those skills.

Advanced Studies. At 2nd level, your knowledge of magic extends beyond the arcane. Choose two 1st-level spells to learn from any spell list. You can cast each of these spells once at its lowest level, and you must finish a long rest before you can cast it in this way again. Your spellcasting ability for these spells is Intelligence.

Wizard School Dropout Arcane Tradition

Wizard Level	Features
2nd	Improvised Spell, Supplementary Abilities
5th	Ability Score Increase
10th	Combat Magic Tactics
14th	Reflexive Magic

Master and Student. Starting at 6th level, your coaching bolsters your allies' spellcasting abilities. When a friendly creature that you see within 30 feet of you casts a spell, and the creature can hear you, you can use your reaction to give the creature advantage on its ranged spell attack roll or to give the target of the caster's spell disadvantage on its saving throw against the spell.

Once you use this feature, you can't use it again until you finish a short or long rest.

Aura of Concentration. At 10th level, while you or friendly creatures within 10 feet of you are concentrating on a spell, you and the creatures have advantage on Constitution saving throws to avoid breaking your concentration.

Aura of Magical Resistance. At 14th level, you and friendly creatures within 10 feet of you have advantage on saving throws against spells.

Wizard School Dropout

Wizarding schools are tough. After all, the average graduation rate for most is below 85%. Of course, just because someone fails at a wizarding school, doesn't mean that they still can't try to wield arcane power, even if they do so poorly.

If you are partaking in a Pexia Academy of the Arcane Arts campaign, at your GM's discretion, you can take this option even if you flunk out of the school.

Improvised Spell. Starting when you choose this arcane tradition at 2nd level, you've learned creative ways to cast spells that most arcane scholars consider "sloppy." Once per turn, you can use your action to expend one spell slot to create an improvised magic spell. The spell is a ranged spell attack with a range of 30 ft and deals 2d10 force damage on a hit. For each spell slot you expend above 1st, you can add one of the following features:

- The spell's range increases by 30 feet, to a maximum of 150 feet.
- The spell's damage increases by 1d10, to a maximum of 5d10.
- The spell can target one additional target within range, to a maximum of 5 targets. You must make a separate ranged spell attack roll for each target.

You may not cast another spell, including cantrips, on the same turn that you use this feature.

Supplementary Abilities. Also at 2nd level, you've learned to supplement your magic with abilities that

Teacher Arcane Tradition

Wizard Level	Features
2nd	Magical Expertise, Advanced Studies
5th	Master and Student
10th	Aura of Concentration
14th	Aura of Magical Resistance

rely on your physical tenacity more than your intellect. You gain one of the following features of your choice:

Danger Sense. You have advantage on Dexterity saving throws against effects that you can see, such as traps and spells. To gain this benefit, you can't be blinded, deafened, or incapacitated.

Jack of All Trades. You can add half your proficiency bonus, rounded down, to any ability check you make that doesn't already include your proficiency bonus.

Mobility. On each of your turns, you can a bonus action on each of your turns in combat. This action can be used only take the Dash or Disengage action.

Ability Score Increase. At 6th level, you can increase one ability score of your choice by 2, or you can increase two ability scores of your choice by 1. As normal, you can't increase an ability score above 20 using this feature.

Combat Magic Tactics. At 10th level, you gain one of the following features of your choice.

Rapid Fire. When you cast a ranged spell attack of 1st level or higher that targets only one creature, you can have it target a second creature. You must roll a separate ranged spell attack roll for each target.

Spell Tag. When you hit a creature with a spell attack, you have advantage on ranged spell attacks against that creature and the creature has disadvantage on saving throws against your spells until the end of your next turn.

Reflexive Magic. At 14th level, you gain one of the following features of your choice.

Retaliatory Spell. When you take damage from a creature that you can see within 30 feet of you, you can use your reaction to expend a 1st-level or higher spell slot. The creature immediately takes 2d10 force damage.

Self-Preservation. You can your action to end one spell on yourself.

New Cantrips from the Pexia Academy of the Arcane Arts

The following cantrips are available on the spell lists for sorcerers, warlocks, and wizards in addition to those normally offered.

Blades
Conjuration cantrip
Casting Time: 1 action
Range: 60 feet
Components: V, S
Duration: Instantaneous
Two daggers appear in front of you. You can direct the daggers at the same target or at different ones. Make a separate ranged spell attack for each dagger. On a hit, the target takes 1d4 piercing damage. The daggers then disappear.

The spell creates more than two daggers when you reach higher levels: four daggers at 5th level, six daggers at 11th level, and eight daggers at 17th level.

Distraction
Enchantment cantrip
Casting Time: 1 action
Range: 15 feet
Components: V, S
Duration: Instantaneous
You create a distracting sound or image, causing a creature of your choice that you see within range and that can perceive the distraction to make a Wisdom saving throw. A creature that can't be charmed succeeds on this saving throw automatically, and if you or your companions are fighting the creature, it has advantage on the save. On a failed save, the target has disadvantage on its Wisdom (Perception) checks until the start of its next turn.

Keyhole
Divination cantrip
Casting Time: 1 action
Range: Touch
Components: V, S, M (a copper key)
Duration: Concentration, up to 1 minute
You touch a non-magical door. An invisible, magical keyhole that only you can perceive appears somewhere on the door. For the duration, you can look through the keyhole to see what is on the other side of the door. Because of the relatively small size of the keyhole, you have disadvantage on Wisdom (Perception) and Intelligence (Investigation) checks to perceive anything on the other side of the door.

A spell that magically locks or wards the door (such as the knock and guards and wards spell, etc.) prevents this spell from working.

Magesword
Transmutation cantrip
Casting Time: 1 action
Range: Touch
Components: V, S, M (a drop of steel polish, a piece of cloth cut from a wizard's robe, and a steel tool such as a fork or butter knife)
Duration: 1 minute
The steel tool you are holding transforms into a longsword. You are proficient with this sword, even if you aren't normally proficient with longswords. For the duration, you can use your spellcasting ability instead of Strength for the attack and damage rolls of melee attacks using the sword. The sword is magical. The spell ends if you cast it again or if you let go of the sword.

Odd Mutation

Transmutation cantrip

Casting Time: 1 action
Range: 15 feet
Components: V, S, M (a toad's eye, a mushroom, and a pinch of paprika)
Duration: Concentration, up to 1 minute

One target that you can see within range must make a Charisma saving throw. On a failed saving throw, you create one of the following magical effects:

The target's skin changes to a color of your choice for the duration.

You alter the appearance of the target's eyes for the duration.

A mushroom, patch of grass, or rough tuft of hair appears on the target's skin and remains for the duration.

The target's voice deepens or softens for the duration.

The target appears ten years older or ten years younger for the duration.

None of the changes have an adverse effect on the creature, although, another creature that witnesses the transformation may see the sudden change as odd.

Repel Projectile

Abjuration cantrip

Casting Time: 1 action
Range: Self
Components: S
Duration: Concentration, up to 1 round

You raise your palm in the air. The next time you are hit by a ranged weapon attack before the start of your next turn, the damage that you take from the attack is reduced by 1d10 + your spellcasting ability.

Scream

Evocation cantrip

Casting Time: 1 action
Range: Self
Components: V, M (a tuning fork)
Duration: Instantaneous

You emit a high-pitched scream, causing damage to creatures and objects in a 15-foot cone. Each creature in that area must make a Constitution saving throw, taking 1d6 thunder damage on a failed save. A creature made of inorganic material such as stone, crystal, or metal has disadvantage on this saving throw.

A nonmagical object that isn't being worn or carried also takes the damage if it's in the spell's area.

The spell's damage increases by 1d6 when you reach 5th level (2d6), 11th level (3d6), and 17th level (4d6).

Sluggish

Transutation cantrip

Casting Time: 1 action
Range: 60 feet
Components: V, S, M (a living slug and a pinch of salt)
Duration: Concentration, up to 1 round

You target one creature that you can within range. For the duration, the creature's speed is reduced by 5 feet.

Skull Bomb

Necromancy cantrip

Casting Time: 1 bonus action
Range: Touch
Components: V, S, M (a Small or Medium humanoid skull is consumed)
Duration: Concentration, up to 1 minute

You touch a non-magical, non-sentient humanoid skull, imbuing it with necromantic energy. You can throw the skull as a ranged spell attack with a range up to 60 feet. On a hit, the target takes 1d6 necrotic damage and the necrotic energy leaps from the target to a different creature of your choice that you can see within 5 feet of it. The second creature takes necrotic damage equal to your spellcasting ability modifier. If someone else attacks with the skull, that attacker adds your spellcasting ability modifier, not the attacker's to the attack and damage rolls. Whether the attack hits or misses, the spell ends on the skull.

If you cast this spell again, the spell ends on any skulls still affected by your previous casting.

This spell's damage increases when you reach higher levels. At 5th level, the skull deals an extra 1d6 necrotic damage to the target and the necrotic damage to the second creature increases to 1d6 + your spellcasting ability modifier. Both damage rolls increase by 1d6 at 11th level and 17th level. Ω

APPENDIX C
OMERIAN GRIMOIRE
BY DAVE HAMRICK
ART BY WHATABOU.ITCH.IO AND GRIFFONS SADDLEBAG

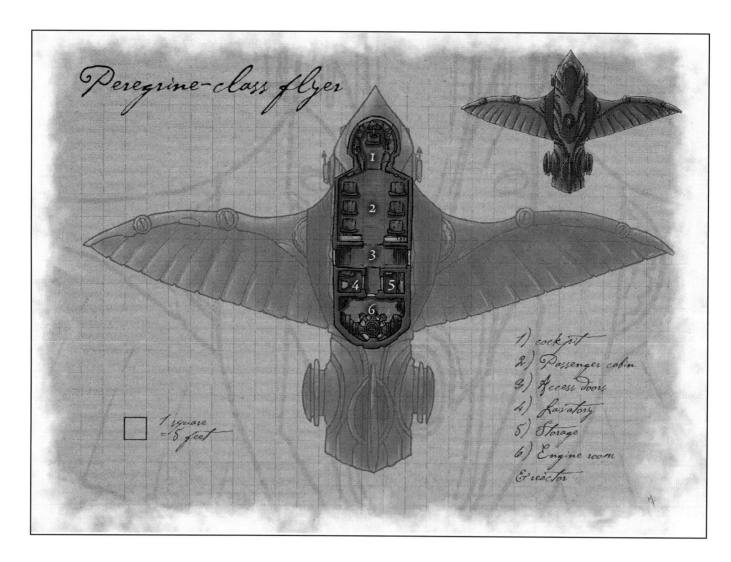

Dinzer Peregrine-Class Flyer

The Peregrine-class flyer is a single-engine high-speed multirole tactical aircraft originally developed by the Shadow Honour artificer guild of Charidge for the Imperial Navy of Odonburg. Designed as a quick-response, air superiority day fighter, it evolved into a successful all-weather multirole tactical aircraft.

A Peregrine-class flyer has the following features:

Ceilings. The ceilings in the fuselage and cabins are 8 feet high with 6-foot-high doorways.

Doors. The flyer's doors are made of wood and have AC 15, 18 hit points, and immunity to poison and psychic damage. A lock can be picked with a successful DC 15 Dexterity check made using thieves' tools, or the door can be forced open with a successful DC 20 Strength (Athletics) check. The controls at the front of the flyer can raise or lower the doors.

Lights. The interior of the flyer is illuminated by permanent *light* spells powered by the flyer's emerald reactor. The flyer also has exterior lights that can create a beam of bright light in a 120-foot cone and dim light for another 120-feet.

1 - Cockpit

The pilot of the flyer sits in the cockpit in the captain's chair. While seated in the captain's chair, the pilot can cast the following spells:

At will: *comprehend languages, scrying* (the sensor is always located in the fuselage and cannot move), *true strike*

1/day: *find the path*

2 - Passenger Cabin

The cabin holds six chairs which can recline, allowing a passenger to rest comfortably in the chair. Each chair has a cubby of nourishment set into the right armrest. The cubby generates a soft, flavorless food tablet that dissolves on your tongue and provides as much nourishment as 1 day of rations and one pint of cold drinking water. Once the cubby generates a food tablet, it can't do so again for 8 hours.

3 - Access Doors.

At both the east and west sides of the flyer's entry, two access doors lower allowing creatures to enter the flyer.

4 - Lavatory

A soft, padded bench with a hole carved in the center fills this room. Below the bench is a chamber pot with a portable hole in its bottom. As soon as waste passes into the chamberpot, and a creature exits through the lavatory door, a *prestidigitation* spell is cast on the creature to clean and disinfect it and remove any unpleasant odors.

5 - Storage

The storage locker is protected by an iron door and has AC 19, 18 points, and immunity to poison and psychic damage. Often, weapons and magic items are stored here.

6 - Engine Room

The engine room has the following features:

Arc Propulsion Engine. The force energy drawn from the emerald Odonburgite within its emerald reactor powers the flyer's Shadow Honour Levi-tech arc-propulsion engine (APE).

Emerald Reactor. The flyer is powered by a Quickshroud 1.87 dl emerald reactor.

Tool Chests. The room includes two tool chests. Both chests act as *bags of holding*, containing enough tools and spare parts to completely rebuild the ship almost from the ground up. The only irreplaceable object is the ship's Emerald Odonburgite crystal.

Minimum Crew. It only takes one crewperson to fly a Peregrine-class flyer, a pilot. Often the pilot is a **mage** with proficiencies in Arcana and Vehicles (air).

PEREGRINE-CLASS FLYER
Gargantuan vehicle (70 ft. by 30 ft., 135 ft. wingspan)

Creature Capacity 1 crew, 6 passengers
Cargo Capacity 4 tons
Travel Pace 220 miles per hour (5,280 miles per day)

STR	DEX	CON	INT	WIS	CHA
20 (+5)	15 (+2)	18 (+4)	0	0	0

Saving Throws Dex +6
Damage Immunities poison, psychic
Condition Immunities blinded, charmed, deafened, exhaustion, frightened, incapacitated, paralyzed, petrified, poisoned, prone, stunned, unconscious

ACTIONS

On its turn, the flyer can take 2 actions, choosing from the options below. It can't take actions if it has no crew.

Fire Eldritch Cannons. The flyer can fire its eldritch cannons.
Move. The flyer can use its helm to move with its wings.
APE Move (Costs 2 Actions). The flyer can use its helm to move with its arc-propulsion engine.

HULL

Armor Class 17
Hit Points 300 (damage threshold 15)

CONTROL: HELM

Armor Class 18
Hit Points 50

Move up to the speed of one of the flyer's movement components. If the helm is destroyed, the flyer can't fire its eldritch cannons.

MOVEMENT: WINGS

Armor Class 15
Hit Points 100; -5 ft. speed per 25 damage taken
Speed (air) 120 ft. (hover)

MOVEMENT: ARC-PROPULSION ENGINE

Armor Class 15
Hit Points 200; -25 ft. speed per 50 damage taken
Speed (air) 500 ft. (on the same turn the flyer uses it action to move 250 ft. or more in one round, attacks made against it are made with disadvantage)

WEAPON: ELDRITCH CANNONS (2)

Armor Class 15
Hit Points 30 each
Ranged Weapon Attack: +8 to hit, range 300 ft., one target. *Hit*: 11 (2d10) force damage.

New Magic Items

Gloves of Amphibios

Wondrous item, uncommon (requires attunement)

These gloves come in many different colors and meld seamlessly into your hands when you don them. While wearing these gloves, climbing doesn't cost you extra movement, you gain a +1 bonus to Strength (Athletics) checks made to grapple a creature, and any creature grappled by you that is not wearing armor takes 1d4 poison damage at the end of each of your turns.

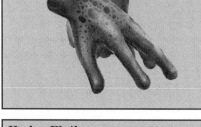

Hydra Flail

Weapon (flail), rare

This flail's spiked head is held in the jaws of a metal hydra figurehead. Whenever you score a critical hit with this weapon against a hostile creature, the weapon magically grows another spiked head. You gain a +2 bonus to damage rolls made with this magic weapon for each head the flail has, up to +6 bludgeoning damage. After 1 hour, any head the flail grows in this way falls off and disappears.

No-Stones

Wondrous item, uncommon

This engraved geode has been split apart into two equal halves. A labyrinth is carved into the rock's rough exterior and glows with a faint light.

While holding one of the halves, you can use an action to speak the geode's command word, "unturned," and turn it over so the flat, gem-encrusted side is pressed against a solid stone, natural metal (such as iron or silver), or earthen surface such as a floor or wall. When you do, the geode becomes magically fixed in place against the surface and projects a 3-foot-spherical map above it, showing the area within 120 feet of it. The map shows all walls, floors, and other surfaces made of either stone, natural metal, or earth within range as translucent outlines and shapes. The map is entirely monochromatic, but shows the general location of any trap or gemstone within its range with a shapeless red glow.

The geode remains fixed in place until you speak its command word again using a bonus action, its surface moves, or it's forced to hold more than 100 pounds. A creature can use an action to make a DC 15 Strength check, moving the geode and causing the map to vanish.

Once a half has been used in this way, that half can't be used again until the next dawn.

"We've been walking in circles for an hour, Gorrin."

The half-orc looked perplexed. "I'm sure that this was the right way, though...."

The dwarf, having had enough, took out a gemstone from his pack. Meliandra looked over to him.

"Oh? Looking at your rocks, again, Dres?"

The dwarf ignored her, placing the gem against the cave floor and muttering a word under his breath.

A spectral map illuminated the dark cave passageway. The corridors and the walls around them appeared, revealing a hidden passage behind a false wall nearby.

"Wow." Muttered Meliandra.

Gorrin stood and contemplated the map, silently. "What are those red lights, Dres?"

Drs picked the stone back up, dismissing the map and stowing it back in his bag. "Either our death or our fortune. Care to find out?"

Headdress of the Serpent King

Wondrous item, uncommon (requires attunement)

This gold and emerald green headdress channels old and twisting serpentine magic to your bidding. If you take poison damage while wearing this headdress, that damage is reduced by your Constitution modifier.

While wearing the headdress, ordinary snakes and snakes with a challenge rating of 1/4 or lower are indifferent toward you and will not attack you unless you threaten or harm them. In addition, you can use an action to cast the animal messenger spell from it, but can only target snakes with it.

Curse. This headdress is cursed, and becoming attuned to it extends that curse to you until you are targeted by the remove curse spell. Removing the headdress fails to end the curse on you. While cursed, your speech is slightly changed: you hiss slightly when pronouncing "s" sounds.

Ah, yessss, I can tell that with thisss, we will make hissstory.

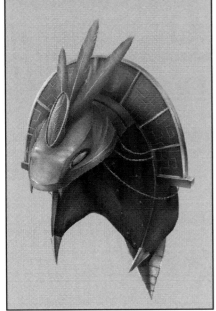

Jaduee-Patr: The Eight Elements of Creation

When Casar was formed, the rogue elemental energies of the Cosmos crashed together and became trapped in a pocket dimension known as the Void. From the void, the unstable energies erupted forming Casar, mortal life, and the Loop.

In time, the energies destroyed each other until only eight forces remained: the foundations of the paths of magic and the elements of creation. These elements became the Jaduee-Patr (Danaavi for "Magic Stones.")

Emerald Odonburgite

Wondrous item, uncommon

The most plentiful of the Jaduee-Patr, emerald odonburgite is the element of evocation. It appears as a glowing-green stone.

A 2-inch diameter piece of emerald odonburgite has 50 charges. While you are holding the emerald odonburgite next to a magic item that has charges, you can use an action to speak a command word to transfer any number of remaining charges from the emerald odonburgite up to the maximum number of charges the magic item can hold.

The emerald odonburgite regains 5d10 charges at dawn.

Ruby Blutvekzelnite

Wondrous item, legendary (requires attunement)

Of all the Jaduee-Patr, ruby blutzvekzlnite is the most unstable and therefore the rarest. It is the Jaduee-Patr element of transmutation.

While you are attuned to a 2-inch diameter piece of ruby blutzvekzlnite you gain the following benefits:

- Darkvision out to a range of 60 feet.
- An increase to speed of 10 feet while unencumbered.
- Proficiency in Constitution saving throws.
- Resistance to acid, cold, fire, light-

ning, and thunder damage.

The first time you attune to the ruby blutvekzelnite and every day at dawn, roll a d100 and refer to the Ruby Blutvekzelnite Changes table on the next page to determine what happens. The changes continue even after you become unattuned to the ruby blutvekzelnite. Only a *greater restoration* spell or similar magic will end the change.

Before rolling on the change table, you can attempt to suppress the changes. Make a DC 15 Charisma saving throw. On a success, you do not change.

Aura of Radiance. The blutvekzelnite emits an aura of radiant energy in a 10-foot radius. Each creature in that area must succeed on a DC 15 Constitution saving throw. On a failed saving throw, the creature becomes poisoned. A creature attuned to the object automatically fails its saving throw. While poisoned, the creature can not regain hit points except through magical means until the poison is cured. A creature attuned to the blutvekzelnite cannot be cured of its poison until it unattunes itself from the gem.

Silingfashi Shi

Wondrous item, rare (requires attunement)

The white gem known as silingfashi shi, or "necromancer stone" is predominantly found on the ashen covered slopes of the volcanic Xenem Dynasty. They are the Jaduee-Patr gems of necromancy.

While attuned to a 2-inch diameter piece of silingfashi shi you gain immunity to necrotic damage and you no longer require food, drink, or sleep. In addition, you become invisible to all undead creatures of CR 2 or lower. You can choose to reveal yourself to any number of undead of your choice without using an action.

Ruby Blutzvekzite Changes.

d100	Change
01-04	You can see invisible creatures.
05-08	You gain the Fire Form trait. Your type becomes elemental and you no longer require air, food, water or drink. You gain immunity to fire damage and vulnerability to cold damage, which replace any other resistances or immunities you already have including those offered by attunement to the ruby blutzvekzite. You can move through spaces as narrow as 1 inch wide without squeezing. A creature that touches or hits you with a melee attack while within 5 of you takes 4 (1d8) fire damage. In addition, you can enter a hostile creature's space and stop there. The first time you enter a creature's space on a turn, that creature takes 4 (1d8) fire damage and catches fire; until someone takes an action to douse the fire, the creature takes 4 (1d8) fire damage at the start of each of its turns. You also shed bright light in a 20-foot radius and dim light in an additional 20 feet. For every 5 feet of water you move into, or for every gallon of water splashed on you, you take 1 cold damage.
09-10	You can cast *magic missile* as a 1st-level spell at will.
11-16	Roll a d10. Your height changes by a number of inches equal to the roll. If the roll is odd, you shrink. If the roll is even, you grow.
17-26	You gain a form of indefinite madness (as described in chapter 8 of the *DMG*).
27-29	You regain 1d6 hit points every 10 minutes, provided that you have at least 1 hit point. If you lose a body part, the body part regrows and returns to full funcitonality after 1d6+1 days if you have at least 1 hit point the whole time.
30-31	You grow feathers which cover your entire body and you gain vulnerability to bludgeoning damage which replaces any other resistances or immunities to bludgeoning damage you may already possess.
32-35	You body constantly oozes a greasy puss. Your Charisma score is reduced by 1. You have advantage on Dexterity (Athletics) checks made to escape grapples.
36-39	Roll a d6. Your shade turns a vibrant shade of the rolled color: 1—red, 2—green, 3—blue, 4—orange, 5—yellow, 6—purple.
40-44	You grow an extra eye. You have advantage on Wisdom (Perception) checks that rely on sight.
45-48	Roll a d6. On a result of 1-3, your size increases by one size category and on a result of 4-6 your size decreases by one size category (as the *enlarge/reduce* spell).
49-50	You hit point maximum increases by 2d10 hit points.
51-55	You turn into a tree. You are incapacitated, can't move or speak, but you are aware of your surroundings; you gain a blindsight out to 10 ft. (blind beyond this radius). Your statistics remain the same, but you gain vulnerability to fire damage and resistance to piercing and bludgeoning damage. These vulnerabilities and resistances replace any similar vulnerabilities, immunities, or resistances you may currently have.
56-60	You can cast *misty step* at will.
61-67	You can cast *levitate* at will, targeting only yourself.
68-72	You grow horns from your head which you can use to make unarmed attacks against creatures within 5 feet of you. On a hit, you deal piercing damage equal to 1d6 + your Strength modifier.
73-74	You lose your mouth and can no longer speak.
75-81	Your skin becomes tough and scaly. When you aren't wearing armor, your AC is 13 + your Dexterity modifier. You can use this natural armor to determine your AC if the armor you wear would leave you with a lower AC. A shield's benefits apply as normal while you use your natural armor.
82-85	Your voice pains those that hear it. Each creature within 30 feet of you that hears you speak must succeed on a DC Constitution saving throw or take 1 thunder damage. The DC is equal to 10 + your Constitution modifier. A creature that succeeds on its saving throw is immune to this effect for 24 hours
86	All humanoids frighten you.
87-88	You become permanently ethereal, as the *etherealness* spell, and cannot return to the Material Plane until a *greater restoration* or similar magic is cast upon you.
89-92	You gain resistance to all damage.
93-98	You glow bright light in a 30-foot radius and dim light for an additional 30 feet. Any creature that ends its turn within 5 feet of you is blinded until the end of its next turn.
99	Your form destabilizes and you collapse into a puddle of lifeless goo. You are dead.
100	You explode; you die instantly and leave no remains behind. Each creature within 30 feet of you when you explode must make a DC 15 Dexterity saving throw or take 4d8 radiant damage on a failed saving throw, or half as much damage on a successful one.

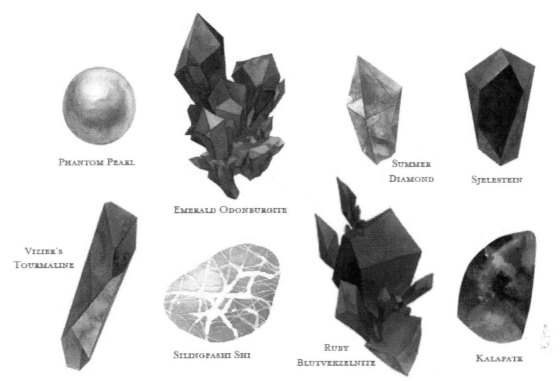

PHANTOM PEARL

EMERALD ODONBURGITE

SUMMER DIAMOND

SJELESTEIN

VIZIER'S TOURMALINE

SILINGFASHI SHI

RUBY BLUTVEKZELNITE

KALAPATR

Summer Diamond

Wondrous item, very rare (requires attunement)

Summer diamonds are found in the Summer Land and used by the Abjurers and Eldritch Knights of Presson's Enclave. They are tied to the element of abjuration.

While attuned to a 2-inch diameter summer diamond, you gain a +2 bonus to AC and immunity to *magic missile*.

Sjelestein

Wondrous item, legendary (requires attunement)

The extremely rare purple crystal sjelestein is found mostly in the northern reaches in Rasgax Highlands. However, the Rasgax are always reluctant to use the material, and instead, choose to guard it within their holds. Sjelestein is the Jaduee-Patr of enchantments.

While attuned to a 2-inch diameter piece of sjelestein, you gain a +2 bonus to your Charisma score and all creatures have disadvantage on saving throws made against your enchantment spells.

Kalapatr

Wondrous item, very rare (requires attunement)

The black summoner's stone of the danaavrakt is what helped the fearsome fiends build their early empire. It is the Jaduee-Patr of conjuration.

While attuned to a 2-inch diameter piece of of kalapatr, whenever you cast a *conjuration* spell that summons creatures, you cast the spell as if it was cast by a slot two levels higher than the one you used (up to 9th level).

For example, if you cast *conjure animals* using a 3rd-level spell slot, you would cast the spell as a 5th-level spell, creating twice the number of creatures you normally would with a 3rd-level spell slot.

Vizier's Tourmaline

Wondrous item, legendary (requires attunement)

Believed by many to not exist at all, vizier's tourmaline is the Jaduee-Patr of divination.

While attuned to a 2-inch diameter piece of vizier's tourmaline, when you cast a divination spell of 2nd level or

higher using a spell slot, you regain one expended spell slot. The slot you regain must be of a level lower than the spell you cat and can't be higher than 5th level. A wizard diviner of 6th level or higher attuned to the stone regains two slots instead of one.

In addition, the vizier has advantage on Intelligence saving throws to avoid the effects of the Strain of Divination (detailed above).

Phantom Pearl

Wondrous item, legendary (requires attunement)

Phantom pearls are the pale yellow stones of the illusionists. Like vizier's tourmaline and ruby blutvekzelnite, phantom pearls are exceedingly rare and believed to no longer exist in Omeria.

While attuned to a phantom pearl, the duration for any illusion spell that you cast increases from 1 minute to 10 minutes, from 10 minutes to 1 hour, from 1 hour to 8 hours, from 8 hours to 24 hours, and from 24 hours to until dispelled. Ω

APPENDIX D
THE BESTIARY
BY DAVE HAMRICK AND ITSADNDMONSTERNOW
ART BY WILLIAM MCAUSLAND, RICK HERSHEY, TITAN FORGE, MIGUEL SANTOS, LUIGI CASTELLANI, AND BODIE HARTLEY

Monster Reference: Grihoo

To run *Grihoo*, you need the Fifth Edition core rulebooks (*PHB*, *DMG*, and *MM*). The Fifth Edition manual of monsters, in particular, will be frequently referenced throughout the adventure. When a creature's name appears in **bold** type, that's a visual cue pointing to that particular rulebook or *Appendix D* (yer lookin at it!). The adjoining table offers an index of all the monsters that appear in *Grihoo* and what location to find them.

Monster Reference Index.

Monster	Reference
amazon warrior	*Appendix D*
cloned sorcerer	*Appendix D*
half red-dragon veteran	*MM*
Heir of Kong	*Appendix D*
knight	*MM*
overgrown clone	*Appendix D*
rakshasa	*MM*
serpent guard	*Appendix D*
shield guardian	*MM*
sorcerer	*Appendix D*
spy	*MM*
stone golem	*MM*
tiger	*MM*
unstable clone	*Appendix D*
young red dragon	*MM*

Amazon Warrior

When the Ivorian Guild first discovered the Serpent Whisperers of Grihoo in the middle of the Ocean of Warna, they dubbed them "Amazon warriors." This name came from the popular legend of the all-female warrior tribes who hailed from the mythical Jungles of Amazonia. Since then, the term has stuck. Armed with thick, obsidian-lined clubs, these warriors of Grihoo race through the dense jungles of the Skeleton Key, eager to combat any who should seek to uncover the secrets of their island protectorate.

AMAZON WARRIOR
Med humanoid (human), lawful neutral

Armor Class 18 (breastplate, shield)
Hit Points 37 (5d8 + 15)
Speed 30 ft.

STR	16 (+3)	INT	9 (-1)
DEX	15 (+2)	WIS	12 (+1)
CON	16 (+3)	CHA	11 (+0)

Saving Throws Str +5, Con +5
Skills Athletics +5, Perception +3, Survival +3
Damage Resistances poison
Senses passive Perception 13
Languages Draconic
Challenge 2 (450 XP)

Capitalize (Once per Turn). If the Amazon hits a creature that she can see with a melee weapon attack, she can use her bonus action to immediately make another melee weapon attack against the same creature. This extra attack has disadvantage.

Fear of Magic. If a creature casts a spell or uses another magical effect within 30 feet of the Amazon and the Amazon can see it, the Amazon must succeed on a Wisdom saving throw with a DC equal to the spellcaster's spell save DC. On a failed saving throw, the Amazon is frightened of the spellcaster for 1 minute. The Amazon can repeat her saving throw at the end of each of her turns, ending the frightened effect on a success. If the Amazon succeeds on her initial saving throw or the effect ends for her, this trait does not function for 1 hour.

Serpent Whisperer. Through sounds and gestures, the Amazon can communicate simple ideas with snakes and other serpents.

ACTIONS

Multiattack. The Amazon makes two attacks with her macuahuitl.

Macuahuitl. *Melee Weapon Attack:* +5 to hit, reach 5 ft., one target. *Hit:* 7 (1d8 + 3) bludgeoning or slashing damage (Amazon's choice), or 8 (1d10 + 3) bludgeoning or slashing damage (Amazon's choice) when wielded with two hands.

Javelin. *Melee or Ranged Weapon Attack:* +5 to hit, reach 5 ft., or range 30/120 ft., one target. *Hit:* 6 (1d6 + 3) piercing damage.

Shield Bash. *Melee Weapon Attack:* +5 to hit, reach 5 ft., one target. *Hit:* 8 (2d4 + 3) bludgeoning damage. If the target is a Medium or smaller creature, it must succeed on a DC 13 Strength saving throw or be knocked prone.

Boy and Man

For twenty-five years, Man has lived on The Skeleton Key as a prisoner of the Serpent Whisperers. The warrior women used him as a zukterin, or breeder, to help propagate their race. He remembers very little before then, but he does remember the tunnels below the temple and the monsters that live there. The only other clue to his history was the large scar on the back of his neck.

One day an explosion erupted from the temple. When the dust settled, a boy emerged, his eyes aglow. Flames shot from the boy's hands and his flesh swirled like water. The Serpent Whisperers, fearful of the supernatural, backed away. The boy then fled into the forest, and Man, seeing his opportunity to escape, followed him. The two have protected each other since. Hundreds of miles from civilization with no formal knowledge of the world beyond the small island, they have very few options.

Like Man, Boy has marks on the back of his neck; but instead of a large scar, Boy's markings are symbols (pictured above) in a language Man does not recognize.

BOY
Small humanoid (unknown), neutral

Armor Class 12 (15 with mage armor)
Hit Points 5 (2d6 − 2)
Speed 30 ft.

STR	7 (-2)	INT	12 (+1)
DEX	14 (+2)	WIS	10 (+0)
CON	9 (-1)	CHA	18 (+4)

Saving Throws Con +1, Cha +6
Skills Arcana +5
Senses darkvision 30 ft., passive Perception 10
Languages Draconic
Challenge ½ (100 XP)

Destructive Magic. Boy can add his proficiency bonus to one damage roll of any sorcerer evocation spell of 1st level or higher that he casts.

Limited Magic Immunity. Boy can't be affected or detected by spells of 3rd level or lower unless he wishes to be. He has advantage on saving throws against all other spells and magical effects.

Innate Spellcasting. Boy's innate spellcasting ability is Charisma (spell save DC 14). Boy can innately cast the following spells, requiring no material components:

At will: *detect thoughts, minor illusion*

Spellcasting. Boy is a 2nd-level spellcaster. His spellcasting ability is Charisma (spell save DC 14, +6 to hit with spell attacks). He knows the following sorcerer spells:

Cantrips (at will): *fire bolt, light, mage hand, prestidigitation*
1st Level (3 slots): *burning hands, magic missile, mage armor*

ACTIONS

Dagger. Melee or Ranged Weapon Attack: +4 to hit, reach 5 ft. or range 20/60 ft., one target. Hit: 4 (1d4 + 2) piercing damage.

MAN
Medium humanoid (human), neutral good

Armor Class 15 (piecemeal armor)
Hit Points 16 (3d8 + 3)
Speed 30 ft.

STR	14 (+2)	INT	16 (+3)
DEX	14 (+2)	WIS	13 (+1)
CON	13 (+1)	CHA	11 (+0)

Skills Arcana +5, Insight +3, Perception +3
Senses passive Perception 13
Languages Common, Draconic
Challenge ½ (100 XP)

ACTIONS

Macuahuitl. Melee Weapon Attack: +5 to hit, reach 5 ft., one target. Hit: 6 (1d8 + 2) bludgeoning or slashing damage (Man's choice), or 7 (1d10 + 2) bludgeoning or slashing damage (Man's choice) when wielded with two hands.

Heirs of Kong

The magic that courses through the veins of The Skeleton Key has had a strange effect on the flora and fauna indigenous to the island. Animals grow larger and are generally more intelligent. Plus, they seemingly possess a greater sense of self. Case in point: the Heirs of Kong. These 12-foot-tall apes inhabit the jungles and forests of the key. And until the Serpent Whisperers of Grihoo arrived, the heirs were the dominant guardians of the island.

Intelligent and psionically active, the heirs do not consider themselves servants of the Serpent Whisperers, rather joint custodians of the island. The heirs even have their own community separate of the Serpent Whisperers. In this community, they

HEIR OF KONG
Large beast, neutral

Armor Class 12
Hit Points 47 (5d10 + 20)
Speed 40 ft., climb 40 ft.

STR		INT	
STR	18 (+4)	INT	9 (-1)
DEX	14 (+2)	WIS	14 (+2)
CON	18 (+4)	CHA	12 (+1)

Skills Athletics +7, Perception +4
Senses passive Perception 14
Languages understands Draconic but can't speak
Challenge 3 (700 XP)

Cunning of Kong. The heir has advantage on saving throws against illusions and enchantments.

ACTIONS

Multiattack. The heir makes two fist attacks.
Fist. Melee Weapon Attack: +7 to hit, reach 5 ft., one target. *Hit:* 12 (2d6 + 5) bludgeoning damage.
Rock. Ranged Weapon Attack: +7 to hit, range 30/60 ft., one target. *Hit:* 12 (2d6 + 5) bludgeoning damage.
Psychic Blast (Recharge 6). The heir emits a violent wave of psychic energy in a 30-foot cone. Each creature in the area must succeed on a DC 12 Intelligence saving throw or take 7 (2d6) psychic damage and become stunned until the end of the heir's next turn.

decide on matters important to both the island and the heirs. Regardless, when the island is challenged, they almost always join forces with the Amazons. Individually, the apes and the warrior women are powerful. But together, they are an unstoppable force of nature.

The original Kong was rumored to be a 30-foot tall ape that lived in the nameless mountain range at the center of the island. However, no proof has emerged that such a creature ever existed. Regardless, the apes still happily carry the moniker.

Clones of Grihoo

Deep beneath a remote island hidden from the world is a temple, dark and terrible. In its construction intertwines terrestrial stone and unknown steel. Within its walls live terrible things that ought not exist. And all of this stands in tribute to an evil entity of tremendous power.

Cloned Sorcerer

Where all the other clones were considered failures, a sorcerer known only as Sixty-Six is the only one to be considered a success.

Every other clone cursed to live out its miserable existence within the walls of the temple of Grihoo is but a shadow of this individual's potential. This cloned sorceror is a capable fighter and adept spellcaster, able to weave and sustain spells in a way not possible for any other mage in existence.

In the *Grihoo* adventure, the clone Sixty-six is a cloned sorcerer.

Overgrown Clone

Those clones which successfully test through the initial phases of their growth then continue to mature to their full intended size. It is at this point that they face the second major failing point along their growth cycle:

nearly all of the clones that reach this phase simply don't stop growing. If an overgrown clone doesn't shatter its own development chamber due to its sheer size, it is ejected and discarded, the same as with the earlier rejects.

While these clones may be larger and more physically developed than their unstable siblings, they are no more advanced mentally. Overgrown clones are similarly violent and prone to fits of rage. With these larger individuals though, their excitable internal magic activates to enhance their growth one hundredfold.

An angered or excited clone such as this will grow uncontrollably, at a rate clearly visible to any observer. While this growth makes the clone undeniably more dangerous, the

CLONED SORCERER
Medium monstrosity, neutral

Armor Class 13 (16 with mage armor)
Hit Points 66 (12d8 + 12)
Speed 40 ft.

STR	DEX	CON	INT	WIS	CHA
12 (+1)	16 (+3)	13 (+1)	11 (+0)	14 (+2)	19 (+4)

Saving Throws Dex +6, Con +4, Cha +7
Skills Deception +10, Insight +8, Perception +5
Senses Darkvision 60 ft., passive Perception 8
Languages Common, Draconic, Infernal
Challenge 6 (2,300 XP)

Sorcery Points. The clone has 10 sorcery points. It can spend 1 or more sorcery points as a bonus action to gain one of the following benefits:

Heightened Spell. When the clone casts a spell that forces a creature to make a saving throw to resist its effects, the clone can spend 3 sorcery points to give one target of the spell disadvantage on its first saving throw made against the spell.

Quickened Spell. When the clone casts a spell that has a casting time of 1 action, they can spend 2 sorcery points to cast the spell as part of the same bonus action used to spend those sorcery points.

Twinned Spell. When the clone casts a spell that targets only one creature and doesn't have a range of self, they can spend a number of sorcery points equal to the spell's level to target a second creature in range with the same spell (1 sorcery point if the spell is a cantrip). Only a spell incapable of targeting more than one creature at the spell's current level is eligible.

Spellcasting. The clone is a 10th-level spellcaster. Its spellcasting ability is Charisma (spell save DC 15, +7 to hit with spell attacks). The clone has the following sorcerer spells prepared:

Cantrips (at will): *acid splash, fire bolt, mage hand, poison spray, ray of frost, shocking grasp*
1st Level (4 slots): *burning hands, mage armor(†), magic missile, shield, thunderwave*
2nd Level (3 slots): *invisibility, misty step, scorching ray*
3rd Level (3 slots): *blink, counterspell, fireball*
4th Level (3 slots): *greater invisibility, wall of fire*
5th Level (2 slots): *dominate person*

ACTIONS

Multiattack. The sorcerer makes two weapon attacks.
Dagger. Melee or *Ranged Weapon Attack:* +5 to hit, reach 5 ft. or range 20/60 ft., one target. *Hit:* 5 (1d4 + 3) piercing damage.
Spell Node (Recharge 4–6). The clone conjures a pulsing node of magic and uses it to sustain a spell. The node appears as a pulsating gray sphere floating in an unoccupied space within 10 feet of the clone. The node has an AC of 12, 20 hit points, and immunity to all nonmagical damage. The clone can have up to 3 spell nodes active at once. As part of this action, the clone spends one of its spell slots to cast a spell that normally requires concentration. The spell is cast as normal, except that the node becomes the spell's origin, the spell doesn't require concentration, and it lasts for its full duration, or until the node is destroyed. Effects of a spell originating from a node end for a target if at any point an uninterrupted 60-foot path can't be traced from the node to that target. A node dissipates if it has no more targets. Spells cast into a node can be augmented by the clone's sorcery points.

REACTIONS

Bend Luck. When another creature the clone can see makes an attack roll, an ability check, or a saving throw, the clone can spend 2 sorcery points to roll 1d4 and apply the number rolled as a bonus or penalty (clone's choice) to the creature's roll.

OVERGROWN CLONE
Large monstrosity, chaotic evil

Armor Class 10 (natural armor)
Hit Points 45 (6d8 + 18)
Speed 30 ft.

STR		INT	
STR	17 (+3)	INT	3 (-4)
DEX	8 (-1)	WIS	7 (-2)
CON	16 (+3)	CHA	9 (-1)

Saving Throws Str +5, Con +5
Senses darkvision 60 ft., passive Perception 8
Languages understands Common but can't speak
Challenge 2 (450 XP)

Runaway Growth. The clone grows each round that it's in combat. Each round at initiative count 0, roll a die. On an even result, the the clone's size increases by one category. Each time the clone grows this way, it regains 20 hit points, and it gains a cumulative +1 bonus to all ability checks, saving throws, as well as attack and damage rolls. When the clone is Gargantuan and would increase its size again, its organs and musculoskeletal structure can no longer support the growth, causing the clone to collapse and die.

ACTIONS

Slam. Melee Weapon Attack: +5 to hit, reach 5 ft., one target. *Hit:* 10 (2d6 + 3) bludgeoning damage.
Hurl Debris. Ranged Weapon Attack: +5 to hit, range 30/90 ft., one target. *Hit:* 8 (1d10 + 3) bludgeoning damage.

transformation is inherently unsustainable. Eventually, the growth exceeds the capacity of the clone's own organs, causing it to collapse and expire as suddenly as the process began.

Unstable Clone

Unstable clones are those which fail the earlier checks along their development. Once it is clear that a clone isn't going to mature properly, the process is halted, and the clone is removed from its development chamber and discarded.

UNSTABLE CLONE
Small monstrosity, chaotic evil

Armor Class 14 (natural armor)
Hit Points 7 (3d6 -3)
Speed 30 ft.

STR		INT	
STR	9 (-1)	INT	10 (+0)
DEX	16 (+3)	WIS	8 (-1)
CON	8 (-1)	CHA	13 (+1)

Skills Acrobatics +5
Senses darkvision 60 ft., passive Perception 9
Languages understands Common but can't speak
Challenge ½ (100 XP)

Unstable Magic. As a bonus action, the clone can attempt to channel its chaotic inner magic. Roll a d8. The clone produces the corresponding effect from the following table:

1. The clone explodes in a burst of flame. The clone is killed, and each creature within 10 feet of it must make a DC 13 Dexterity saving throw, taking 7 (2d6) fire damage on a failed save, or half as much on a successful one.

2–3. Nothing happens. The clone can't use its Unstable Magic again until it completes a short or long rest.

4. A random creature within 30 feet of the clone ceases to exist, vanishing in a puff of smoke. At the start of that creature's next turn, it reappears in the closest unoccupied space to a point 2d10 feet in a random direction from where it vanished.

5. Until the end of the clone's next turn, its speed increases by 15 feet, it can move through the spaces of creatures larger than it, and it doesn't provoke opportunity attacks for leaving an enemy's reach.

6. The clone teleports up to 30 feet to an unoccupied space it can see.

7. The clone makes an elemental surge attack.

8. The clone rolls on this table at the end of each of its turns, even if it had already used its unstable magic that turn. This continues until the clone rolls a result of 1–3 for this ability at any point.

ACTIONS

Dagger. *Melee or Ranged Weapon Attack:* +5 to hit, reach 5 ft. or range 20/60 ft., one target. *Hit:* 5 (1d4 + 3) piercing damage.

Elemental Surge. *Melee or Ranged Spell Attack:* +3 to hit, reach 5 ft. or range 60 ft., one target. *Hit:* 4 (1d6 + 1) acid, cold, fire, or lightning damage (clone's choice or determined randomly).

Most of these stunted and misshapen beings die within hours. Those which do not grow to be feral, mad, and violently unpredictable. Their underdeveloped minds and traumatic emergence are a volatile mix, as nearly all of these clones are creatures of frustrated rage which lash out at the slightest provocation.

Unfortunately (for themselves, as well as those around them), these clones' proclivity for rage and violence quickly excites the magical forces inherent in their bodies, resulting in potent and highly random bursts of magic.

Bufonem

Resembling large, distorted toads with a third eye in the center of the bulbous foreheads, the bufonems were the dreaded servants of Loikiel. In the late 6th century, after Loikiel was defeated by the danaavrakts, the bufonem fled Aspaeth. Using their humanoid disguises, they took to rural areas where many still hide. Even today the witchhunters of Aspaeth travel Omeria seeking the toadfolk of Aspaeth. On more than one occasion, the witchhunters have set fire to entire villages caught hosting the depraved creatures.

Doppelganger Foes. Although they share a common origin, doppelgangers despise bufonems. To make matters worse, the two can see each other for what they truly are. As such, the Aspaethan witchhunters frequently employ doppelgangers in their ranks to spot the toadsfolk in their humanoid disguises.

The Cult of Dhucabra. It's been over 400 years since the bufonems worshipped the Transmuter Loikiel. The sages among the toadfolk have since turned their attention to the myth of Dhucabra, a titan believed to be the Father of Transmutation. They have yet to find the titan.

BUFONEM
Medium monstrosity (shapechanger), neutral evil

Armor Class 13 (natural armor)
Hit Points 33 (6d8 + 6)
Speed 30 ft., swim 40 ft.

STR	16 (+3)	INT	10 (+0)
DEX	14 (+2)	WIS	10 (+0)
CON	13 (+1)	CHA	9 (-1)

Skills Perception +4
Damage Immunities bludgeoning, piercing, and slashing from nonmagical attacks not made with redstone
Senses Darkvision 60 ft., passive Perception 14
Languages Common, Infernal
Challenge 2 (450 XP)

Shapechanger. The bufonem can use its action to polymorph into a Medium humanoid, or back into its true form which is a toad-humanoid hybrid. The bufonem's humanoid form is always the same, and its statistics are the same in each form. Any equipment it is wearing or carrying isn't transformed. It reverts to its true form if it dies.

Amphibious. The bufonem can breathe air and water.

Keen Sight. The bufonem has advantage on Wisdom (Perception) checks that rely on sight.

Standing Leap. The bufonem's long jump is up to 30 feet and its high jump is up to 15 feet, with or without a running start.

ACTIONS

Multiattack. The bufonem makes two attacks, only one of which can be its bite or its tongue.

Bite (Hybrid Form Only). *Melee Weapon Attack:* +5 to hit, reach 5 ft., one target. *Hit:* 6 (1d6 + 3) piercing damage.

Claws (Hybrid Form Only). *Melee Weapon Attack:* +5 to hit, reach 5 ft., one target. *Hit:* 5 (1d4 + 3) slashing damage.

Mace (Humanoid Form Only). *Melee Weapon Attack:* +5 to hit, reach 5 ft., one target. *Hit:* 6 (1d6 + 3) bludgeoning damage.

Tongue. *Ranged Weapon Attack:* +5 to hit, range 15 ft., one target. *Hit:* 6 (1d6 + 3) piercing damage. If the target is Medium or smaller, it is grappled (escape DC 13), pulled up to 15 feet toward the bufonem, and restrained until the grapple ends. The bufonem can grapple one target at a time with its tongue.

Heads of Grihoo

Each one merely an aspect of the immortal titan Grihoo, its innumerable heads are always active, and always hungry.

Grihoo's individual heads defy the laws of reality, able to reach nearly any distance, as they are seemingly of infinite length. It's impossible to identify where one head's long neck begins, as Grihoo's swirling mass is constantly writhing and shifting: the very embodiment of Grihoo is that of an infinite tangle of serpents.

Grihoo will extend these heads to execute its will as quickly and as effortlessly as one would extend an arm to retrieve an object from a nearby table. The heads each appear to be fully autonomous, as if they were individual creatures, yet completely aware of the surroundings of every other, like an inseperable hive mind.

And while any individual head can be slain, do not mistake this for vulnerability. After all, what use is it when each can be replaced a hundredfold, out to infinity?

Legion. Though each of Grihoo's individual heads can be become a discrete snake-like organism, they all share a single consciousness. As such, each Head of Grihoo shares its knowledge and perception with the greater entity (and therefore all of its other heads) at all times.

HEAD OF GRIHOO
Large fiend, neutral evil

Armor Class 14 (natural armor)
Hit Points 45 (7d10 + 7)
Speed 30 ft., swim 30 ft., climb 5 ft.

STR		INT	
STR	18 (+4)	INT	11 (+0)
DEX	15 (+2)	WIS	14 (+2)
CON	13 (+1)	CHA	14 (+2)

Skills Stealth +4, Perception +4
Damage Vulnerabilities slashing from magic weapons
Damage Resistances acid, poison; bludgeoning, piercing, and slashing from nonmagical attacks
Condition Immunities charmed, poisoned, unconscious
Senses blindsight 15 ft., darkvision 60 ft., passive Perception 14
Languages Draconic, understands all other languages, telepathy 120 ft.
Challenge 3 (700 XP)

Acid Blood. Whenever the Head of Grihoo suffers piercing or slashing damage, each other creature within 5 feet of it takes 1 acid damage.

Hydra Rejuvenation. If the Head of Grihoo dies from slashing damage, it splits and returns to life as two Heads of Grihoo at the start of its next turn unless fire is applied to the remains. Each of these Heads of Grihoo return with half their hit points.

Pack Tactics. The Head of Grihoo has advantage on an attack roll against a creature if at least one of the Head of Grihoo's allies is within 5 feet of the creature and the ally isn't incapacitated.

ACTIONS

Bite. Melee Weapon Attack: +6 to hit, reach 10 ft., one target. *Hit:* 9 (2d4 + 4) piercing damage.

Constrict. Melee Weapon Attack: +6 to hit, reach 5 ft., one target. *Hit:* 11 (2d6 + 4) bludgeoning damage, and the target is grappled (escape DC 14). Until this grapple ends, the creature is restrained, and the Head of Grihoo can't constrict another target.

Orner Wreros

Orner Wreros is a wildly intelligent gnomish inventor and wizard. His actions led to the crash of *The Predator* in the adventure **The Flight of the Predator**.

At some point before the events of the **Grihoo** adventure, Orner escapes into the forests. During his time in the forest, he discovers the remains of a Dinzer science vessel, *The Hyderabad*, that wrecked on the island a century ago. Within the hull of the vessel, Orner discovers a remote

ORNER WREROS
Small humanoid (gnome), neutral evil

Armor Class 13
Hit Points 54 (12d6 + 12)
Speed 25 ft.

STR		INT	
STR	7 (-2)	INT	18 (+4)
DEX	16 (+3)	WIS	9 (-1)
CON	11 (+0)	CHA	14 (+2)

Saving Throws Int +6, Wis +1
Skills Arcana +6, Deception +4, Perception +1
Senses darkvision 60 ft., passive Perception 11
Languages Common
Challenge 1 (200 XP)

Gnome Cunning. Orner has advantage on all Intelligence, Wisdom, and Charisma saving throws against magic.

ACTIONS

Multiattack. Orner makes two weapon attacks.

Dagger. Melee or *Ranged Weapon Attack:* +5 to hit, reach 5 ft. or range 20/60 ft., one target. *Hit:* 5 (1d4 + 3) piercing damage.

traveler juggernaut suit. As the characters struggle to survive the difficult conditions of the island, Orner starts rebuilding the suit...

JUGGERNAUT ORNER
Huge humanoid (gnome), neutral evil

Armor Class 18 (juggernaut suit)
Hit Points 114 (12d12 + 36)
Speed 30 ft., fly 60 ft.

STR		INT	
STR	19 (+4)	INT	18 (+4)
DEX	5 (-3)	WIS	9 (-1)
CON	17 (+3)	CHA	14 (+2)

Saving Throws Int +6, Wis +1
Skills Arcana +6, Deception +4, Perception +1
Damage Resistances fire; bludgeoning, piercing, and slashing from nonmagical attacks that aren't made from adamantine weapons
Senses darkvision 60 ft., passive Perception 11
Languages Common
Challenge 6 (2,300 XP)

Magic Resistance. Orner has advantage on saving throws against spells and magical effects.

Siege Monster. Orner deals double damage to objects and structures.

ACTIONS

Multiattack. Orner makes two slam attacks.

Slam. Melee Weapon Attack: +7 to hit, reach 10 ft., one target. *Hit:* 14 (3d6 + 4) bludgeoning damage.

Chest Cannon (Recharge 6). Ranged Weapon Attack: +6 to hit, range 40/120 ft., one target. *Hit:* 10 (3d6) bludgeoning damage. Hit or miss, the target and each creature within 20 feet of it must make a DC 14 Dexterity saving throw, taking 10 (3d6) fire damage on a failed save, or half as much on a successful one.

Serpent Whisperer Snakes

The Serpent Whisperers of Grihoo have a natural kinship with serpents. Through simple gestures and hissing sounds, they can communicate with snakes and direct them to perform simple tasks.

In addition to the anacondas, cobras, and other snake varieties that exist on The Skeleton Key, the island is also home to two unique serpents: lava cobras and needleblast boas.

Lava Cobra

Although the nameless mountain's three volcanoes haven't erupted in centuries, magma still courses through The Skeleton Key's veins. Slithering out of the Key's magma tubes are lava cobras, 12-foot-long serpents that can breathe fire as well as any Aegreyan half-blood.

LAVA COBRA			
Large monstrosity, unaligned			

Armor Class 15 (natural armor)
Hit Points 37 (5d10 + 10)
Speed 30 ft.

STR	17 (+3)	INT	1 (-5)
DEX	15 (+2)	WIS	10 (+0)
CON	14 (+2)	CHA	3 (-4)

Damage Immunities fire
Senses blindsight 10 ft., darkvision 60 ft., passive Perception 10
Languages —
Challenge 3 (700 XP)

Multiattack. The lava cobra makes two bite attacks.

Bite. *Melee Weapon Attack:* +5, reach 5 ft., one creature. *Hit:* 6 (1d6 + 3) piercing damage plus 3 (1d6) fire damage.

Fire Breath (Recharge 5-6). The cobra exhales fire in a 30-foot line that is 5-feet wide. Each creature in that area must make a DC 12 Dexterity saving throw, taking 21 (6d6) fire damage on a failed save, or half as much damage on a successful one.

Needleblast Boa

Named for the dense copse of spikes that jut from just below their jaw lines, needleblast boas are a common sight in Grihoo Village. Combining some of the most dangerous elements of the island's most poisonous snakes as well as its largest constrictors, a needleblast boa's bite is capable of blinding and incapacitating most humanoids.

The boas who live among the Serpent Whisperers subsist on a steady diet of goats, chickens, and the occasional violator of the Serpent Whisperers' code of law.

NEEDLEBLAST BOA			
Large beast, unaligned			

Armor Class 15 (natural armor)
Hit Points 30 (4d10 + 8)
Speed 30 ft., swim 30 ft.

STR	15 (+2)	INT	1 (-5)
DEX	14 (+2)	WIS	10 (+0)
CON	14 (+2)	CHA	3 (-4)

Senses blindsight 10 ft., passive Perception 10
Languages —
Challenge 2 (450 XP)

ACTIONS

Bite. *Melee Weapon Attack:* +4, reach 5 ft., one creature. *Hit:* 5 (1d6 + 2) piercing damage plus 9 (2d8) poison damage and the target must succeed on a DC 12 Constitution saving throw or become poisoned. While poisoned, the creature is blinded. The creature can repeat its saving throw at the end of a long rest, ending the poisoned and blinded effects on a success.

Constrict. *Melee Weapon Attack:* +4 to hit, reach 5 ft., one creature. *Hit:* 6 (1d8 + 2) bludgeoning plus 9 (2d8) piercing damage and the target is grappled (escape DC 14). Until this grapple ends, the creature is restrained, and the boa can't constrict another target.

Serpent Guard

The Serpent Whisperers of Grihoo (or "Amazons" as they're commonly known) protect the Shrine of Grihoo and its ancient secrets long lost to the world. The actual entrance to the shrine is protected by the legendary Serpent Guard, the fiercest warriors of their kind. Each member of the Serpent Guard wields the powerful tepoztopilli, a polearm topped with a broad wooden head capable of crushing enemy spines with a single blow. The tepoztopilli gives the serpent guards the advantage of reach while allowing them to use their massive tower shields for added defense.

SERPENT GUARD
Med humanoid (human), lawful neutral

Armor Class 18 (breastplate, shield)
Hit Points 76 (9d8 + 36)
Speed 30 ft.

STR		INT	
STR	18 (+4)	INT	9 (-1)
DEX	14 (+2)	WIS	14 (+2)
CON	18 (+4)	CHA	12 (+1)

Saving Throws Str +7, Dex 5, Con +7, Wis +5
Skills Athletics +7, Perception +5, Survival +7
Damage Resistances poison
Senses passive Perception 15
Languages Draconic
Challenge 5 (1,800 XP)

Capitalize (Once per Turn). If the Amazon hits a creature that she can see with a melee weapon attack, she can use her bonus action to immediately make another melee weapon attack against the same creature. This extra attack has disadvantage.

Fear of Magic. If a creature casts a spell or uses another magical effect within 30 feet of the Amazon and the Amazon can see it, the Amazon must succeed on a Wisdom saving throw with a DC equal to the spellcaster's spell save DC. On a failed saving throw, the Amazon is frightened of the spellcaster for 1 minute. The Amazon can repeat her saving throw at the end of each of her turns, ending the frightened effect on a success. If the Amazon succeeds on her initial saving throw or the effect ends for her, this trait does not function for 1 hour.

Serpent Whisperer. Through sounds and gestures, the Amazon can communicate simple ideas with snakes and other serpents.

Shield Guardian. When the Amazon takes the Dodge action and she is wielding a shield, she gains a +3 bonus to her AC.

ACTIONS

Multiattack. The Amazon makes three attacks with her tepoztopilli.

Tepoztopilli. Melee Weapon Attack: +7 to hit, reach 10 ft., one target. *Hit:* 8 (1d8 + 4) bludgeoning damage, or 9 (1d10 + 4) bludgeoning when wielded with two hands.

Sling. Ranged Weapon Attack: +5 to hit, range 30/120 ft., one target. *Hit:* 4 (1d4 + 2) piercing damage.

Shield Bash. Melee Weapon Attack: +7 to hit, reach 5 ft., one target. *Hit:* 11 (2d6 + 4) bludgeoning damage. If the target is a Medium or smaller creature, it must succeed on a DC 15 Strength saving throw or be knocked prone.

Sorcerer

As descendants of the dragonkin of Aegraya and the Great Chromatics of The Summer Land, sorcerers are creatures born with innate magical powers. Anthroposcopic features such as yellow eyes, scales, and sharp features often betray the sorcerer's origins. As such, those who are without an innate ability to obscure such features are often viewed as outcasts, just as if they were half-dragons or dragonborn.

Children of Tostrasz. Of all the Chromatic breeds who mixed with humanoids, reds were by far most prolific. Tostrasz the Enormous alone was rumored to have over 100 half-humanoid progeny.

The Drakeblood Colony. Maer is a cliff-side, coastal colony found east of Vaskil on the other side of the Spine. There, the drakebloods live free from persecution of the Pressonians who remember all too well the War of the Burning Plains.

Drakebloods in Omeria

Humanoids who possess draconic blood come in three variants. The actual children of dragons and humanoids are half-dragons. Second generation drakebloods are dragonborn. And third-generation drakebloods are humanoids who have a proclivity to sorcery (for example, a human with the draconic bloodline sorcerous origin). Although, it's rare for fourth-generation drakebloods to possess sorcerous power, it's not impossible. Beyond fourth-generation, the draconic blood runs too thin to grant magical abilities.

SORCERER
Medium humanoid (any), any alignment

Armor Class 15 (natural armor)
Hit Points 75 (10d8 + 30)
Speed 30 ft.

STR	DEX	CON	INT	WIS	CHA
8 (-1)	14 (+2)	14 (+2)	10 (+0)	12 (+1)	18 (+4)

Saving Throws Con +5, Cha +7
Skills Deception +7, Intimidation +7
Senses passive Perception 11
Languages Draconic plus any two languages
Challenge 5 (1,800 XP)

Draconic Bloodline. The sorcerer's draconic bloodline increases its maximum hit points by 10 (included in its hit points). In addition, whenever the sorcerer makes a Charisma check when interacting with dragons, its proficiency bonus is doubled.

Elemental Affinity. When the sorcerer cats a spell that deals fire damage, it can add its Charisma modifier to one damage roll of that spell. At the same time, it can spend 1 sorcery point to gain resistance to that damage type for 1 hour.

Metamagic. The sorcerer has 10 sorcery points. it regains all its spent sorcery points when it finishes a long rest. It can spend its sorcery points on the following options:

Careful Spell. When the sorcerer casts a spell that forces other creatures to make a saving throw, the sorcerer can spend 1 sorcery point and choose up to three creatures. A chosen creature automatically succeeds on its saving throw against the spell.

Empowered Spell. When the sorcerer rolls damage for a spell, it can spend 1 sorcery point to reroll a number of the damage dice up to its Charisma modifier (minimum of one). It must use the new rolls. The sorcerer can use Empowered Spell even if it has already used a different Metamagic option during the casting of the spell. Quickened Spell. When the sorcerer casts a spell that has a casting time of 1 action, the sorcerer can spend 2 sorcery points to change the casting time to 1 bonus action for this casting.

Spellcasting. The sorcerer is a 10th-level spellcaster. Its spellcasting ability is Charisma (spell save DC 15, +7 to hit with spell attacks). It knows the following sorcerer spells:

Cantrips (at will): fire bolt, light, mage hand, message, minor illusion, prestidigitation
1st Level (4 slots): burning hands, magic missile, shield
2nd Level (3 slots): darkness, invisibility, scorching ray
3rd Level (3 slots): counterspell, fireball
4th Level (3 slots): dimension door, wall of fire
5th Level (2 slots): cone of cold

ACTIONS

Dagger. *Melee* or *Ranged Weapon Attack:* +5 to hit, reach 5 ft. or range 20/60 ft., one target. *Hit:* 4 (1d4 + 2) piercing damage.

Grihoo Player Map

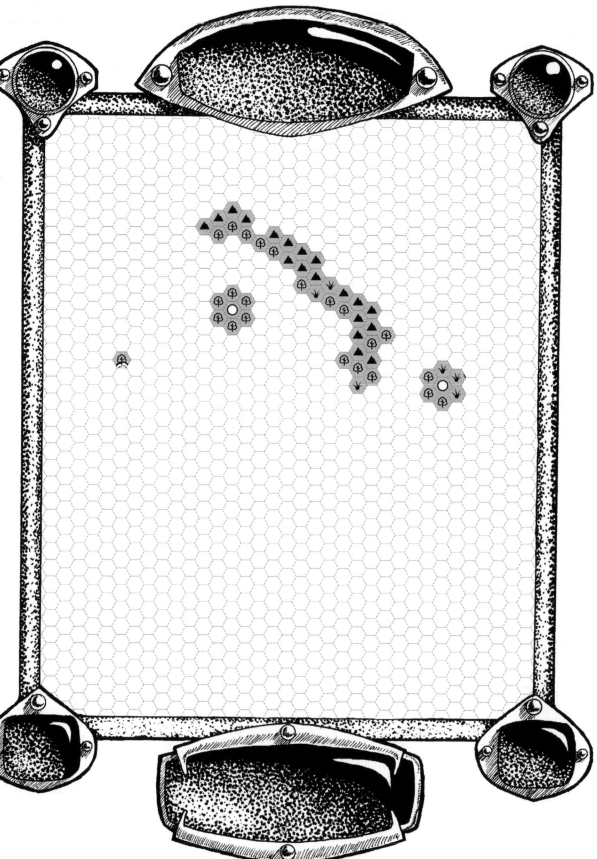

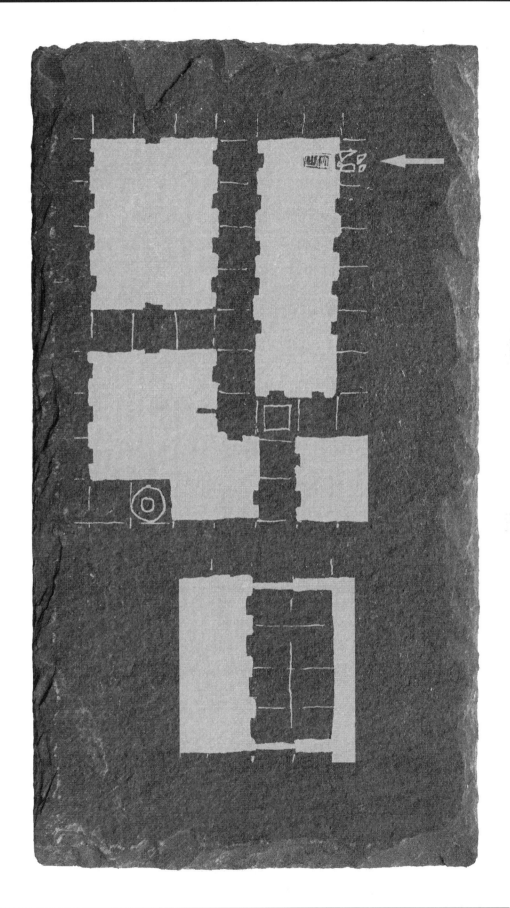

Grihoo Strange Diagram

Grihoo Temple Map

Grihoo Abandoned Mine

OPEN GAMING LICENSE

Made in the USA
Middletown, DE
25 August 2020

16809937R00073